Beyond Restructuring

A collection of papers from a King's Fund international seminar

Beyond Restructuring

A collection of papers from a King's Fund international seminar

Edited by Sholom Glouberman

Published by
King's Fund Publishing
11–13 Cavendish Square
London W1M 0AN

ISBN 1 85717 112 8

A CIP catalogue record for this book is available from the British Library

Distributed by Bournemouth English Book Centre (BEBC)
PO Box 1496
Poole
Dorset
BH12 3YD
Tel: 0800 262260
Fax: 0800 262266

Origination by Trigon Press, Beckenham, Kent
Printed and bound in Great Britain

Cover image: Annabel Obholzer

Contents

List of participants

Jennifer Alexander
General Superintendent
NSW Health Department
Sydney, Australia

Peter Brennan
Commissioner of Health
Health Dept of Western Australia
Perth, Australia

Diana Horvath
Chief Executive Officer
Central Sydney Area Health Service
Camperdown, Australia

Brendon J Kearney
Chief Executive
Royal Adelaide Hospital
Adelaide, Australia

Dody Bienenstock
Department of Psychiatry
Faculty of Health Sciences
McMaster University
Hamilton, Canada

John Bienenstock
Dean & Vice-President
Faculty of Health Sciences
Hamilton, Canada

Ann Casebeer
Department of Community Health Sciences
Faculty of Medicine
The University of Calgary
Calgary, Canada

Michael Decter
APM Management Consultants Inc.
Toronto, Canada

Marie Fortier
Executive Director
National Forum on Health
Ottawa, Canada

Sholom Glouberman
Fellow
King's Fund College
Toronto, Canada

Sarah Prichard
Associate Dean
Faculty of Medicine, McGill University
Montreal, Canada

Don Schurman
President & CEO
University of Alberta Hospitals
Edmonton, Canada

Hon. Louise Simard
McPherson, Leslie & Tyerman
Regina, Canada

Kevin Smith
Vice-President
Community Health & Academic Affairs
St Joseph's Community Health Centre
Hamilton, Canada

Lester Levy
Chief Executive Officer
South Auckland Health
Auckland, New Zealand

Karen O Poutasi
Chief Advisor and General Manager
Planning & Advisory Division, ICOA
Wellington, New Zealand

William Pick
Head of Department
Department of Community Health
University of Witwatersrand
Johannesburg, South Africa

Tim Wilson
Special Adviser to the Minister of Health
Department of Health
Pretoria, South Africa

Gordon Best
Fellow
King's Fund College
London, UK

J S Bradbrook
Chief Executive
Wigan & Leigh Health Services NHS Trust
Wigan, UK

Frank G Burns
Chief Executive
Wirral Hospital
Merseyside, UK

Jenny Griffiths
Chief Executive
Hertfordshire Health Agency
Herts, UK

Peter Griffiths
Director
King's Fund College
London, UK

Ken Jarrold
Director of Human Resources
NHS Executive
Leeds, UK

Robert Maxwell
Chief Executive
The King's Fund
London, UK

David Moss
Chief Executive
Southampton University Hospitals NHS Trust
Southampton, UK

P D Wright
Consultant Surgeon and Medical Director
Freeman Hospital
Newcastle Upon Tyne, UK

Jo Ivey Boufford
Deputy Assistant Secretary for Health
Dept Health & Human Services
Washington, USA

Nan Carle
Fellow
King's Fund College
Chevy Chase, USA

John G King
President & CEO
Legacy Health System
Portland, USA

James J Mongan
Executive Director
Truman Medical Centre
Kansas City, USA

Mary Jo O'Brien
Health Policy Consultant
Senior Fellow at the School of Public Health
University of Minnesota
St Pauls, USA

Thomas G Rundall
Professor & Director
Graduate Programme in Health Services Management
University of California
Berkeley, USA

List of contributors

Jennifer Alexander
General Superintendent
NSW Health Department
Sydney, Australia

Peter Brennan
Commissioner of Health
Health Department of Western Australia
Perth, Australia

Marie Fortier
Executive Director
National Forum on Health
Ottawa, Canada

Sarah Prichard
Associate Dean
Faculty of Medicine, McGill University
Montreal, Canada

Don Schurman
President & CEO
University of Alberta Hospitals
Edmonton, Canada

Hon. Louise Simard
McPherson, Leslie & Tyerman
Regina, Canada

Tim Wilson
Special Adviser to the Minister of Health
Department of Health
Pretoria, South Africa

Frank G Burns
Chief Executive
Wirral Hospital
Merseyside, UK

Jenny Griffiths
Chief Executive
Hertfordshire Health Agency
Herts, UK

Peter Griffiths
Director
King's Fund College
London, UK

Ken Jarrold
Director of Human Resources
NHS Executive
Leeds, UK

Robert Maxwell
Secretary & Chief Executive
King's Fund
London, UK

P D Wright
Consultant Surgeon and Medical Director
Freeman Hospital
Newcastle upon Tyne, UK

Frederick D Alley
President & CEO
The Brooklyn Hospital Center
New York, USA

John G King
President & CEO
Legacy Health System
Portland, USA

James J Mongan
Executive Director
Truman Medical Centre
Kansas City, USA

Foreword

The past decade or so has been an unsettled period in the health services of many countries. The commonest problem has been about funding, as economic growth has slowed, while the capacity of the health sector to absorb more money shows no sign of diminishing. Since much of the money comes in one way or another from public sources, governments have everywhere been involved in interventions in the health care system, many of them structural, and invariably labelled as 'reforms', with the implication that the new ways are better than the old.

This book comprises papers and discussions from 30 leaders in the health systems of six countries, all of which have undergone, or are undergoing, major attempts at reform. The central question posed to all who took part was, 'When your country has completed its programme(s) of structural change, where will you need to focus your attention in relation to health policy, health care and the management of the health care system?' The assumption behind the question is that structural changes, even if well conceived and well executed, will not solve all our difficulties, and that we do not want to be swept down a road of continued further structural changes in pursuit of the mirage of a perfect, trouble-free system.

One thing that stands out from the book is what it feels like currently to be in positions of influence and responsibility in the health sector, with old assumptions and certainties breaking down, and important issues needing to be tackled in real time in one's own job or institution, wherever the system at large may be headed. While we can learn some things from one another, we should resist any urge to hand out panaceas – for example, to the South Africans who face such a dramatic need to make their health care arrangements more effective and fairer for the majority, and to do so fast, within extremely tight financial constraints.

Among the tentative answers to that broad question about what lies beyond restructuring was a shared interest in working across organisational and professional boundaries in our fragmented health care systems; in developing common agendas, even where there are professional differences of interest and of view; and in building collaborative networks and alliances among very diverse individuals and agencies. The hard part, of course, is not in the theory but in actually doing these things in practice, which is where the experience of practitioners reflected in this book is of greatest value.

Robert J Maxwell
Secretary and Chief Executive
King's Fund

Acknowledgements

This book needed a lot of help. Many people have participated in it. The attendees of the King's Fund International Seminar contributed papers before the seminar, and lots of debate and ideas during it. The papers that were submitted were of a high quality and we would have liked to include more of them in the book itself. Unfortunately there was only room for a small number. We have tried to select those that married the themes that were assigned before the seminar, with the ideas expressed at the meetings.

Many people who were not at the seminar collaborated in the preparation of the book in other ways.

Richard James of the Severn NHS Trust contributed stories and support during the editorial process. We gratefully acknowledge the financial support for the editing from a number of people and institutions: Steven W Herbert of Baycrest Centre for Geriatric Care, Toronto, Richard Higgins of Parkside Health, London, Peter Ellis of Sunnybrook Health Science Centre Toronto and now of Gemini Consultants in London, and, of course, Peter Griffiths of the Management College at the King's Fund, London.

There were others who cannot all be mentioned who read and commented on the text, transcribed articles, or contributed ideas, stories or other suggestions. Most significant among them were: Femida Allaedera, Miriam Sostaric, David Ryan, Sheila Damon, Shelley Ditty, Nigel Roome, Larry Peterson, Alex Katz, Alan Engelstad and Susan Glouberman. Members of the consulting seminar in Toronto had to listen to some of the ideas in this book when they were only half-baked. Students and colleagues at the University of Toronto also suffered during the birth pangs of the book. Sandy Leggat, who taught with me on the Strategic Management course, and the students on that course, were especially involved in helping me try out some of the ideas on the ground. The Organizational Development department at Sunnybrook and The Group of Seven at Baycrest have provided a basis for some post-structural interventions.

Meredith Lee did the punishing work of preparing the text for publication and assisting me on a variety of writing, rewriting, and research tasks. Her help has been invaluable. David Gershater proofread the text.

Robert Maxwell took time to read the text carefully and to suggest changes which have improved it.

I would like to thank the production team, which includes Minuche Mazumdar, Giovanna Ceroni, Katie Stone, and Judith Sheppard. Thanks also to Annabel Obholzer for the painting.

I take responsibility for the errors and omissions, misconceptions, and misunderstandings ... and all the other bad things that come back to haunt me in the night.

Sholom Glouberman
Toronto, July 1996

One of our kinsmen, Nya Nganas, went out hunting one day when suddenly it became foggy and he could not see to find his way home. Eventually he came upon a stream which seemed to have appeared from nowhere. He tried to jump over the stream but fell into the water and sunk to the depths until he came to the world beneath the water.

He found himself in a land barren of life. Finally, he saw a girl riding on a strangely-coloured reindeer. He ran after her and asked her which tribe she was from but she did not seem to hear him. He caught up to her and touched her lightly on the shoulder and asked who she was. Feeling his touch the girl cried out in pain as though someone were stabbing her. Confused as to why the girl could not hear him, Nya Nganas tapped her again.

'A spirit has pricked my shoulder,' she cried.

Nya Nganas thought this was very strange and decided to follow the girl. When they came to a village of four or five chooms, the girl was still in great pain. She entered one of the chooms and Nya Nganas followed her in. She was so sick that when people asked what had happened she was unable to explain. Nya Nganas felt very sorry for her and he tried to comfort her by wrapping her in his parka, but she only shrieked in pain even more loudly.

Meanwhile the fire crackled and hissed as if a presence were in the room. The people in the choom asked themselves why the fire was behaving so. It was decided that a spirit sickness had entered their choom and that a shaman must be called to save the girl.

The shaman was a wise old man and after weaving his spells he told them that after three days the girl would get better. But after three days of lying in fever, she was worse than before. All the while Nya Nganas sat in a corner unseen by everyone.

Finally the girl's father said, 'Our daughter is doomed, the old shaman could do nothing for her. Somewhere I've heard there is a young orphan who has become a shaman. Let us summon him.'

The girl's brother was sent to fetch the young shaman. The shaman first ate, then methodically began to dress himself in the shaman's garb, every few minutes glancing in the direction of Nya Nganas. Nya Nganas thought to himself, 'This shaman knows that I am here.' And in fear, he tried to hide behind the girl, pressing his face close to her back. The shaman peered behind the girl as he began to beat his drum. He started to chant loudly, and told the girl that she had the sickness of kofa nguo.

The orphan-shaman turned to Nya Nganas and said, 'Why is it that you cling to this girl so tightly? Leave her alone, you are tearing her soul. What do you want? We will give you anything, but let the girl go.'

Nya Nganas said that he wanted the strangely coloured reindeer that he had first seen with the girl. 'Give me that and I will leave right away.'

The orphan-shaman told the girl's father that the sickness spirit would leave as soon as he was given the strangely-coloured reindeer and the father consented at once. The young shaman ordered the people of the tribe to begin building a reindeer out of wood. They set to work and decorated the wooden reindeer with charred wood from the fire.

When the reindeer was ready, the shaman began beating his drum and jumping up and down as though he were running fast. Nya Nganas, lost in the sound of the drum, thought to himself that the people had prepared the reindeer for him and that he must ride it away from this place. He mounted the wooden reindeer and rode away from the choom.

Meanwhile the young shaman played his drum and danced in circles around and around until he fell to the ground exhausted. At that same moment across the plain and far from the choom, Nya Nganas stopped suddenly. As he looked around, he realised that he was on a wooden reindeer, at the same stream bank where he had fallen into the water.

'What sort of shaman could have done this to me?' he thought to himself. 'The old shaman did not have any power and did not see me, but the young orphan shaman was very strong, and he made me lose my senses.'

Nya Nganas went back to his kin to tell them of his adventures. He told them they were all sickness spirits: piercing ones, sicknesses of fever, of smallpox and others. He warned them that one day they could end up in the other world and be confronted with the clever orphan-shaman who would not let them go.

And then they all turned into sickness spirits, they were no longer people. Since that day, if someone is sick, people say that one of Nya Nganas' people has come, and if the shaman cannot help, it is because he is like the weak old shaman. But if a spirit encounters an orphan-shaman then it will be seen and the spirit won't be able to steal a single soul.

Introduction

How to read this book

The King's Fund International Seminar has met for almost two decades. Every two years, representatives of English-speaking countries gather to explore a theme in health care. The meetings have been characterised by the early identification of major issues, and intense debate about them. They have challenged long-standing and dearly held assumptions. They have also given senior health care executives new ideas, new friends and the experience of visiting another country. The seminar in 1995 was held in Banff, Alberta, Canada and there were representatives from Canada, the UK, the USA, Australia, New Zealand and, for the first time, South Africa.

Each participant submitted a paper on the general theme 'Beyond Reform, What?' for distribution to the rest of the attendees. During the meetings, the papers formed a background for the discussions. We have assembled some of the papers into a book which traces the discussions and the conclusions of the conference. In the past, these books have been timely explorations of current topics in health care. We hope that this one continues that tradition.

Participants were asked to consider what might happen after the reforms in their countries were implemented. Only some of the papers have been included because of limited space and because the book also contains a summary of the conference discussions, as well as a few of its conclusions.

The book can be read in four different ways:

One can read individual contributions

Before the seminar all participants were asked to submit papers that responded to the theme. The contributions were wide-ranging, and many were passionately either for or against particular changes. We selected representative papers from the participant countries. We tried to choose those that respond to the theme and that can be read as individual comments on those aspects of restructuring which might be of broader interest. One can choose to read only those papers which are of particular interest.

One can read through to capture the flow of discussion

The book organises the papers to try to capture how the discussions went at the meetings. None of the papers was actually presented although many were referred to or summarised. The flow of discussion indicated the areas of agreement and disagreement among participants. The first section of the book is called, 'Some dimensions of restructuring'. It includes eight papers which display some of the similarities and differences between the views of participants, and the directions of reform of their various countries.

As the discussion progressed, it became apparent that the sub-theme of fragmentation in health care was emerging. There were divisions between different providers, then between providers and the public, and finally between the health care of Aboriginal peoples and the rest of the population. The second part of the book, called 'Divisions and splits after restructuring', includes several papers which illustrate this fragmentation. We have organised them to follow the direction of the discussions. A paper by Robert Maxwell summarises the view that restructuring by itself has neither healed these divisions nor resolved other problems in health care.

Towards the end of the seminar, discussions began to look at how to change relationships in health care after restructuring. Part 3 is called 'Some ways forward'. There seemed to be a consensus that restructuring by itself was not sufficient and that further efforts would be needed to close the difficult splits in health care. The development of networks made up of different provider organisations, the recognition of the need for participation in decision-making by more participants, the need to reduce duplication and to improve links; all suggest that new ways of relating and working must be considered. We have therefore concluded the book with several essays which identify a broader range of interested parties who can contribute to healing the fragmentation in health care.

One can read the comments to think beyond restructuring

Editor's comment: the editorial commentary, on the grey panels throughout the book, can be read separately. It is an attempt to structure an argument that accompanies the flow of discussion at the seminar. It traces the increased pressures on health care systems in most countries by looking at: the growth in specialised chimneys of health care knowledge; the inflation of costs; and the need to constrain expenditure on health care everywhere. It tries to present some of the reasons for the fragmentation in health care and to describe some of its consequences. Finally, it concludes with some indications of the next steps to resolve these differences. The editor's comments about each of the papers aim to place the papers in the context of this longer discussion.

One can read the stories and anecdotes

We have chosen a folk tale from Siberia as a frontispiece to illustrate how differences in culture can force us to understand things more slowly. These differences pose questions that are hard to answer and they can leave some mystery behind. Why does the hero of the story assume the identity of a sickness spirit so easily? Why do only some of the people see him? Are we like the hero – unwitting sickness spirits? Is there anything else to learn from the story?

The story mirrors several of the issues raised at the seminar and in the book. One is about the different cultures inside health care. Doctors, nurses, managers and others have different education, values, attitudes, and tell different stories. A second is about the difference between health care for native people and for the dominant groups in affluent societies. The health status and the care provided for native peoples is significantly worse than for any other group in wealthy nations. Is this because providing health care across cultural boundaries poses special problems? A third is that hearing new stories and anecdotes can force us to reframe old problems and see them in a new light.

We have all heard many discussions about restructuring. We have all been through it. Many of us have developed very partisan views which can make it more difficult to hear others. Telling some stories that slow us down might help us think about the issues in a fresh way. We have included stories and anecdotes about health care and health care-related issues to emphasise these points. The stories in the book will add emphasis or provide contrast to the rest of the argument.

1 *Some dimensions of restructuring*

Part 1 provides a discussion of these questions:

- *should health care organisations be centralised or decentralised?*

- *managed care: pro or con?*

- *who leads … hospitals or primary and community care?*

The theme of the last King's Fund International Seminar was 'Beyond Reform, What?'. The papers and discussions showed an increasing diversity of opinion about health, health care, and the professions, institutions, and systems involved in all areas of health-related human services.

Each country represented at the seminar was changing the structures and financing for health care but there was no clear agreement on the impact of these reforms, or what would follow them. There was, however, agreement that health care was fragmenting and needed integration.

To begin this book, we present three snapshots of the state of the professions, organisations and systems in health care, over the last 70 years or so. The snapshots can help us make sense of the most recent reforms and they might give us some idea of where things are headed. They are in the tradition of Foucault who speaks of a history that tells us how we got to where we are – mostly how we got into our present fix.

We also tell a story about a hospital apple orchard which can supplement our history. Stories can give the flavour of the changing perspectives on health care and even substitute for more linear argument.

The 'Good Old Days' (1935)

We have strong cultural memories of the good old days. When we think about good health care we remember the kindly old GP, a well known and respected member of our community who cared for us from the cradle to the grave, often with the help of a dedicated nurse. The doctor was always there when we needed him. We could go to his house where a room served as his office or he would come to ours if we had a fever. He would provide everything from stitches, to help with home births, to life advice. He always had time. Money was never an issue and there were few bills – the doctor was paid at the door in cash. Often there was little that he could do except be there, but his caring attitude and availability were deeply valued. He has almost completely disappeared, though he remained as a character in Hollywood movies, comics, and on television until well into the sixties.

Someone pointed out that even this memory is not universal. People from the middle class share this kind of memory of the individual practitioner, but immigrants, working class people and the poor tended to receive their health care from public clinics in hospitals even then.

Doctors and nurses also do not really agree about the hospitals of the good old days. Nurses remember when the hospital was controlled by the matron and was a place to nurse and care for those who could not afford to be cared for in their homes. The nurse would make the decision to call for the doctor when medical attention was needed. Doctors on the other hand remember when the general hospital was run by the medical superintendent. Michael Gordon, the chief of Medicine at Baycrest, revealed that, 'Some of us call those days 'G.O.D.'. And that is what the chief doctor was.' He (almost invariably the medical superintendent was a man) controlled everything about the hospital: all aspects of its operation were under his direction.

The hospital was typical of many institutions of the day: extremely hierarchical with one person who had a very wide range of authority. An excellent picture of the time emerges from contemporary descriptions of other institutions such as schools:

> *In the organisation of the graded school, there are the principal, the assistants, and the pupils. Each is necessary to make the school, but in the functioning of the school the principal is more important than the assistants, and the assistants than the pupils. The members of the system vary in importance.* (Kirkpatrick, 1932. p24)

In the hospital, the superintendent had absolute authority over every aspect of the operations. The Matron was his helpmate, and the administrator, if there was one, worked as his aide. There were no strong internal boundaries separating the various staff members. The main border was to the outside at the hospital entrance. Upon entering the hospital, every patient came under the authority of the medical superintendent, much as pupils were under the ultimate authority of the principal of the school.

The Hospital's Apple Orchard 1935

The hospital is run by the Medical Superintendent. Full-time employees do all the maintenance and service work. There are, for example, three roofers, who do nothing except replace roof tiles; an upholstery shop; a chief gardener and grounds keeper and so on. Many of these people live on hospital property.

The medical superintendent likes apple crumble ...

He has an orchard planted on the grounds which is cared for by the grounds keeper. It takes several years until the apples appear and when they do, everyone praises the medical superintendent's foresight. Some of the staff, especially those who live on the hospital grounds, take a few of the apples for themselves and their friends. The medical superintendent is fiercely proud of his apples and declares that anyone stealing them will be sacked. This becomes the rule of law in the hospital, and no one takes any of the apples for themselves.

The catering staff makes excellent apple crumble and the medical superintendent enjoys it for many years until well after his retirement.

The values of the organisation are clear to everyone and not questioned – they are derived from the central over-arching authority of the medical superintendent. Some of this authority derives from the knowledge (and wisdom) attributed to him. His knowledge is based on extended and

cont.

cont.

intelligent clinical experience. Medical education comes from a lengthy clinical apprenticeship. And the Medical Superintendent embodies the sum of this kind of knowledge through experience. He is not just the final arbiter of decisions, he makes them all. There is no long-term planning, or any need for it: he just does whatever he feels is necessary. If there *are* any plans, they are in his head.

Because the hospital is usually built and funded by the community, it is a major social institution. Many communities identify themselves through the creation of their hospital. Its independence from external authority, and its special place in the community allowed it to remain relatively stable for a long time. The social place of the hospital gives the Medical Superintendent status and prominence in the community that enlarges his authority even more.

There is widespread agreement about the roles of doctors and hospitals, and this occurrs without a formal government-run health care system. Everyone seems to agree on the values associated with health care and health care professionals.

The 'Good Old Days' (1955)

After the Second World War, there was a burst of new effort in health care. For many reasons, including the condition of recruits during the war and of returning veterans after it, there was a strong concern about the health status of the population.

In Britain, the creation of the National Health Service reflected a widespread belief that universally accessible, comprehensive and free health services now would result in a diminishing need for them in the future. The NHS was, to some extent, an investment in a government service that would improve the health of the nation. It was believed that if it became successful, its cost would diminish in time.

In most countries, the war showed that we could acquire useful knowledge more quickly by a kind of division of intellectual labour. An investment in scientific research would bear the fruit of better health care results. There was a significant increase in funding for medical education and research. More money for hospitals and universities began to flow.

Lots of doctors were trained. If they were family doctors, they found that there was more to know, and more was beginning to be possible. In hospitals they found that the organisation had begun to change. The division of labour in the acquisition of knowledge meant that there were more holders of knowledge than in the past. Knowledge came from research results as well as from direct experience. There was much more research activity, almost entirely by physician researchers, and growing knowledge about particular areas. The medical superintendent stopped being the source of all knowledge and there was growing differentiation of function. This, in turn, made it possible (and perhaps necessary) to decentralise authority.

The Hospital's Apple Orchard 1955

The hospital has preserved its tradition of home-grown apple crumble. The orchard is in full production. The anti-theft rule has become deeply respected: no one steals the apples. The first crumble of the season is still tasted by the now-retired medical superintendent. He pronounces it 'perfect'.

Indeed, the apples are better than ever, because the chief gardener has new and better orchard equipment. The kitchen staff has expanded to include a pastry chef who is now responsible for preparing the old recipe.

The retired medical superintendent is greeted by the new medical director, who tells him of the expansion contemplated for the hospital and everyone assures him that the apple crumble is and will remain a tradition of the hospital. But the medical superintendent seems to be more comfortable with the three chiefs (Medicine, Surgery, Obstetrics) who are clinicians like he was. Together they talk about recent advances in medicine and changes in clinical practice.

Although the hospital remained hierarchical, doctors began to aspire to become chiefs of departments rather than medical superintendents. The job of director of the hospital, though it remained medical, was becoming more administrative. The director was at the top of a hierarchical chain of command, rather than the font of all wisdom as in the past. He did not (and could not) take major decisions about the hospital without consulting the chiefs. In this departmental bureaucracy, some departments were more important than others. Most activities were regularised into departments which were either clinical (more important) or supportive of the clinical work (less important).

It was at this time that one could begin to see the creation of internal boundaries separating different departments, disciplines, and services. There was only a minimum of rivalry between these departments and services, because the world was expanding. More money was being added to the pot all the time. It was a time of growth, expansion and differentiation.

A Chief of Medicine, who began to practice during this period, told me that medical knowledge and clinical practice were, of necessity, incremental and progressive. They required constant new investment to maintain the pace of advance. He feared that if funding didn't increase, the progress of medical science would end. His view of progress in health care and medicine was typical of this period of 'Good Old Days', and more money kept coming in.

The end of the 'Good Old Days': differentiation run wild

Investments in all areas of health care knowledge led to increasing specialisation in medicine and the creation of a vast array of differentiated professionals in clinical and non-clinical areas of health care. New fields of health care came into existence, each with its own body of knowledge, its own credentials, its own values and perspectives on health care and health care-related issues.

In medicine, the number of specialties, departments and services increased. In North America, even general practice became differentiated into specialties: children routinely went to the paediatrician, the family doctor became an internist or a specialist in family practice.

In hospital medicine, departments began to include divisions and to add specialties and then sub-specialties all of which had unique fields of knowledge. Ophthalmology became differentiated into more than five sub-specialties including at least two related to the retina. A recent brochure from the Toronto Hospital lists, for the benefit of primary care doctors, the 100 different specialty clinics now operating in the hospital (see Table 1).

The same phenomenon occurred in nursing. The Royal College of Nursing in London identifies more than 70 different specialised nursing areas, each of which carries its own knowledge base and skills (see Table 2).

The clinical professions and technical support staff, apart from doctors and nurses, also increased. They all gained specialised knowledge and training. Each came with special skills, expertise and the right to perform certain clinical acts. Many acquired post-graduate training. Some became specialised even within their profession, for example psychiatric social workers, or neuro-psychologists. Research associated with teaching hospitals was increasingly done by non-physicians in specialised areas such as electronic imaging, molecular biology, or bioethics.

In addition, the rest of the work force also began to develop specialised roles and responsibilities so that everyone from clerical staff to accountants had their own job title. The result is that the number of job classifications in hospitals has become enormous. At a teaching hospital in Toronto, we found that there are 420 job titles, each of which has a unique job description (see Table 3).

A major differentiation between the clinical and non-clinical areas of hospitals occurred once professional managers began to administer the hospital. The medical superintendent was no longer in charge of the hospital. Increasingly lay managers became the Chief Executive Officers. Many saw themselves as professionals with post-graduate degrees in Hospital Administration. There was a similar differentiation of specialist staff in human resources, finance, risk management, public affairs, information management, staff education, and so on.

Outside the hospital, there were also more community-based health care personnel who were neither doctors nor nurses. A variety of physical and

Table 1 Toronto Hospital Clinic Listing (total = 99)

Cardiac/Vascular Centres
General Cardiology
Congenital Cardiac Centre
Hypertrophic Cardiomyopathy
Cardiovascular Surgery
Cardiac Rehabilitation
Hypertension
Vascular Centre
Neurosciences
Peripheral Nerve
Brain Tumour
Brain Arterio-Venous
  Malformation
Spinal Cord
General Neurology
Neuro-Otology
Neuro-Ophthalmology
Neuro-Pharmacology
Movement Disorders
Swallowing Centre
Neuro-Laryngology
Neuro-Physiology (EEG, EMG,
  and Evoked Potentials)
Transplantation
Renal
Liver
Lung
Heart
Oncology and Haematology
Lung Cancer
Breast Cancer
Leukaemia
Multiple Myeloma
Lymphoma
Coagulation Disorders
Melanoma
Autologous Blood & Marrow
  Transplant
Genito-Urinary Cancer
Head and Neck Cancer
Gynaecological Cancers
Brain Tumours
GI Cancer
General Surgery
Gastroenterology
Therapeutic Endoscopy

Asthma Centre
Cardio-Respiratory Sleep
  Disorders
Obstetrics & Gynaecology
Obstetrics
Pre-Natal Diagnosis
Special Pregnancy
Reproductive Biology
In-Vitro Fertilisation
Therapeutic Abortion
Gynaecology
Gynaecology Research Clinic
Urology
General Urology
Oncology
Impotence
Prostate Centre
Renal Transplantation
Stone
Voiding Dysfunction &
  Incontinence
Plastic Surgery
Hand Program
Plastic Surgery Clinics
Orthopaedics
Fracture Clinic
Rheumatology
Endocrinology
General Endocrine
Diabetes Clinic
Lipids
Bone Disease
Endocrine Oncology
Thyroid
Pituitary, Adrenal, or Ovary
Anaesthesia
Pain
Malignant Hyperthermia
ENT
ENT Clinics
Neuro-Laryngology
Ophthalmology
Dentistry
Psychiatry
General Psychiatry
Medical Psychiatry

Assessment Clinic
Psycho-Pharmacology
Competency
Group Program
Portuguese Community Mental
  Health Centre
Kensington Clinic
Neuro-Psychiatry
Neuro-Pharmacology & Epilepsy
Tourette's Syndrome
Sleep Disorders
Women's Clinic
Schizophrenia
Other Medical Clinics
General Internal Medicine
Medical Consultation
Dermatology
Family Medicine Centre
Immuno-deficiency
Travel
Tropical Disease
Chiropody
Thalassemia/Sickle-cell
Rehabilitation
Sexually Transmitted Disease
Herpes Info Line
Weight Control
Detoxification

psychological therapists, such as chiropodists, orthoptists, audiologists, and optometrists worked in community settings as primary practitioners. They have all received special training and brought other sources of knowledge to their work. This list does not include the even wider range of alternative medicine practitioners who,

Table 2 Royal College of Nursing Professional Groups (total = 72)

Mental Health
Mental Health Nursing Society
Community Mental Health
  Nursing Forum
Psychodynamic Nursing Forum
Substance Misuse Nursing Forum
Forum for Nurses Working in a
  Controlled Environment
Child and Adolescent Mental
  Health Nursing Forum
Cognitive and Behavioural
  Pschyotherapy
Occupational Health
Cancer Nursing Society
Leukaemia and Bone Marrow
  Transplant Nursing Forum
Palliative Nursing Group
Breast Care Nursing Forum
Women's Health
Midwifery Society
Family Planning Nursing Forum
Gynaecological Nursing Forum
Fertility Nurses' Forum
Nursing Practice
Cystic Fibrosis Nurses' Forum
Diabetes Nursing Forum
Ophthalmic Nursing Forum
Critical Care Nursing Forum
Accident and Emergency Nursing
  Association
Rheumatology Nursing Forum
Society of Orthopaedic Nursing
Stoma Care Nursing Forum
Radiology/Cardiology Nursing
  Forum
Respiratory Nurses' Forum

Blood Transfusion Nursing Forum
Dialysis and Transplant Nurses'
  Forum
Haemophilia Nurses' Association
Transplant Nurses' Forum
Continence Care Forum
HIV Nursing Society
Ethics Forum
Rehabilitation Nurses' Forum
Perioperative Nursing Group
Children
Society of Paediatric Nursing
Paediatric Community Nursing
  Forum
Paediatric Intensive Care Nurses'
  Forum
Paediatric Nurse Managers' Forum
Paediatric Oncology Nursing
  Forum
Community
Health Visitors' Forum
Practice Nurses' Association
School Nurses' Forum
Community Practice Teachers'
  Forum
Community Nursing Association
District Nurses' Forum
Liaison and Discharge Planning
  Nurses' Association
TB Nurses' Forum
Nurse Practitioner Forum
Education
Association of Nursing Education
Higher Education Forum
Education Support Nurses' Forum
Community Health Tutors' Forum

Continuing Education Teachers'
  Forum
Elderly People
Association for the Care of Elderly
  People
Focus on Older People, Nursing
  and Mental Health
Society of Nurse Inspectors and
  Registration Officers
Management
Nurses in Management
Hospice Nurse Managers' Forum
Forum for Independent Nurse
  Managers (INFORM)
Occupational Health Managers'
  Forum
Residential Care Managers' Forum
Nursing Agencies Administrators'
  Forum
Chief Nurses to Health Authorities
NHS General Managers' Forum
Community Nurse Managers'
  Forum
People with a Learning Disability
Society of Nursing for People with
  a Learning Disability
Community Nursing Forum for
  People with a Learning
  Disability
Forum for Nurse Tutors in
  Learning Disability Studies
Miscellaneous
Research Advisory Group
Pain Forum
Complementary Therapies in
  Nursing Group

though dramatically differentiated from orthodox medicine, claim a knowledge base which is more ancient and holistic.

Even outside health care organisations, and apart from all clinical practice, there are numerous experts who have gained highly specialised health care knowledge. There are academics who engage in teaching and research in such areas as hospital administration, health economics, health demographics, and medical sociology. Among the non-academics are policy analysts and planners at various levels of different health care systems, and insurance or government staff who monitor, regulate and administer payments to health care providers. Specialist consultants provide knowledge about everything from shared governance to hospital construction, to computerising the allocation of nursing skills, to cost engineering.

Table 3 Sunnybrook Health Science Centre Job Classification Titles (total = 420)

Accountant	Carpenter	Electronics Technol.	Inter. Scientist
Accounts Payable Clerk	Catering Office Asst	EMG Technician	Intern/Resident
Acting	Charge Nurse	Employee Services Rep.	Interviewer
Administrative Analyst	Chart Abstractor	Engineering Assistant	Jr Research Asst 1
Admin. Asst	Chief Artist	Epidemiologist	Jr Research Asst 2
Admin. Asst I	Chief of Service	Executive Assistant	Jr Research Tech
Admin. Asst II	Chief Operating Engineer	Executive Chef	Jr Research Technol.
Administrative Clerk	Chief Perfusionist	Executive Secretary	Jr Sous Chef
Admin. Co-ordinator	Claims Analyst	Expeditor	Junior Bookkeeper
Admin. Director	Cleaner	Facilities Planner	Junior Buyer
Admin. Secretary	Cleaner Lead Hand	Financial Analyst	Junior Clerk
Admitting Clerk	Clerk Cashier	Financial Analyst III	Junior Clerk Typist
Adolescent Worker	Clerk Messenger	Food Service Cashier	Junior Programmer
Agency – attendant	Clerk Receptionist	Funding Officer (c/l)	Junior Scientist
Agency – nurse	Clerk Typist	G U Orderly	Kitchen Helper
Agency – RNA	Clinical Admin.	Garbage Handler	Laboratory Assistant
Aide	Clinical Data Co-ordinat.	Gardener	Laboratory Helper
Aide Lead Hand	Clinical Dietician	Gardener-Grounds-	LAN Administrator
Air cond./Vent. Mech.	Clinical Engineer	person	Laundry Helper 1
Ambubus Driver	Clinical Expert	General Artist	Laundry Helper 2
Animal Facility Attn. 1	Clinical Nurse Specialist	General Manager	Laundry Helper 3
Animal Facility Attn. 2	Clinical Researcher	Geriatrician	Liaison Officer
Animal Health Technol.	Clinical Researcher (ICIS)	Graduate Psychologist	Librarian
Ann. Giving Telemrktg	Co-op Student	Graphic Artist	Library Assistant
Officer	Co-ordinator	Graphic Designer	Library Technician
Appointments Clerk	Communications Officer	Groundsperson	Library Technician 2
Apprentice	Computer Operator	Head Teacher	Maintenance Helper
Assembly Technician	Conference Asst 1	Health Care Aide	Maintenance Mech.
Assistant	Conference Asst 2	Health Educator	Maitre d' (Vaughan
Assistant Biochemist	Consultant	Health Record Admin.	Estate)
Asst Campaign Dir	Controller	Health Record Tech.	Manager
Asst Co-ordinator	Cook 1	Hearing Aid Dispenser	Mgr Communications
Asst Department Head	Cook 2	Helper Power Plant	Manager, Computing
Assistant Director	Cook Lead Hand	Host/Hostess	Mgr Construction
Assistant Supervisor	Cook's Assistant	Hostel Receptionist	Mgr of Accounts
Asst Systems Manager	Crèche Aide	House Manager	Mgr Policy & Implement.
Asst Teaching Chaplain	Data Analyst	(S Estates)	Mgr Research
Assistant to Chief	Data Co-ordinator	Human Resource Asst	Co-ordinators
Assistant to Director	Data Entry Co-ordinator	I V Technician	Mgr Technical Team
Associate Dept Head	Department Clerk	Ices – Fee for Service	Materials Hand
Assoc. Executive Dir	Department Head	Infection Control Nurse	Materials Lead Hand
Associate Manager	Department Manager	Informatics Officer	Materials Handler 1
Asst Banquet Serv. Mgr	Deputy Director	Information Centre	Medical Artist
Attendant	Development Officer	Specialist	Med. Transcriptionist
Audiologist	Dialysis Technician	Information Co-ordinator	Menu Clerk
Audiologist II	Director	Ins./Fixed Assets Analyst	Morgue Attendant
Autopsy Room Tech.	Dir Research Trans Unit	Installer (Life Style)	Neurophysiologist
Banquet Services Mgr	Discharge Planner	Instructor	Non-registered Nursing
Bar Attendant	Dispatcher	Insurance Clerk	Asst
Behavioural Therapist	Doppler Technician	Inter. Research Asst 1	Nurse Clinician
Biochemist	Driver	Inter. Research Asst 2	Nurse Researcher
Biomedical Engineer	Driver Mechanic	Inter. Research Tech.	Nursing Admin.
Biomedical Ethicist	ECG Technician	Inter. Research Technol.	Nursing Mgr eve/night
Biostatistician	Educator	Interior Designer	Nursing Orderly
Biostatistician 2	EEG Technician	Intermediate Accountant	Nutrition Systems Tech
Buyer	Electrician	Intermediate Clerk	Nutrition Technician
Capital Equipment Clerk	Electronics Tech.	Intermediate Programmer	O R Booking Clerk

O R Booking Clerk 2
O R Technician
Occupational Health
  Doctor
O T 1
O T 2
Oper. Engineer class 2
Oper. Engineer class 3
Oper. Engineer class 4
Operations
  Co-ordinator
Order Processing Clerk
Pacemaker Tech II
Painter
Pastry Chef
Pathology Assistant
Patient Care Mgr I
Patient Care Mgr II
Patient Rel. Officer
Patient Rep.
Payroll Clerk
Payroll Officer
Perfusionist
Personnel Rep.
Pharmacist 1
Pharmacist 2
Pharmacist 3
Pharmacy Technician
Photographer
Physio Training Instruct.
Physiotherapist 1
Physiotherapist 2
Planning Assistant
Plaster Room Tech
Plasterer
Plumber
Pool Attendant
Porter
Porter Escort
Print Machine Oper.
  Helper
Print Machine Oper.
  Lead Hand
Print Machine Operator
Prof. Practice
  Leader/CNS
Prof. Practice
  Leader/Edctr
Professional Practice
  Leader
Program Assistant
Program Director
Program Planner
Program Specialist
Programmer Analyst
Programmer Analyst I
Programmer Analyst II

Project Accountant
Project Devt Nurse
Project Engineer
Project Leader
Prosthetic/Orthotic
  Uncertified
Prosthetic/Orthotic Tech.
Prosthetist/Orthotist
Psychiatric Worker
Psychologist
Psychometrist 1
Psychometrist 2
Public Affairs Officer
Public Information Asst
Pulmonary Function
  Tech.
Quality Assurance
  Admin.
Radiation Physicist
Receptionist
Records Clerk
Recreation Therapist
Reg. Orthopaedic
  Technol.
Registry – Attendant
Registry – Nurse
Registry – RNA
Rehabilitation Aide
Rehabilitation Counsellor
Remedial Assistant
Research Analyst
Research Assistant
Research Associate
Research Co-ordinator
Research Database
  Developer
Research Fellow
Research Tech. 1 (jr)
Research Tech. 2 (inter)
Research Tech. 3 (sr)
Research Technol. 1 (jr)
Research Technol. 2
  (inter)
Research Technol. 3 (sr)
Resource Centre
  Co-ordinator
Respiratory Assistant
Respiratory Therapy Asst
Restorative Pros. Asst
Restorative Prosthetist
S S R Attendant
S S R Attendant Ld Hand
S S R Lead Hand
Safety Advisor
Safety Assistant
Sales Representative
Scientist

Sctry to Exec. VP
Sctry Stenographer 1
Sctry Stenographer 2
Sctry to Asst VP
Sctry to Director
Sctry to Directory
Sctry to Head of Serv.
Sctry to Medical Staff
Secretary to VP
Section Leader
Security Officer
Sr Accounting Clerk
Sr Accounts Payable
  Clerk
Senior Admin. Clerk
Sr Admitting Clerk
Senior Audiologist
Senior Billing Clerk
Senior Biostatistician
Senior Clerk Cashier
Sr Neurophysiologist
Sr Nursing Orderly
Sr Pharmacy Tech
Sr Programmer Analyst
Sr Research Asst 1
Sr Research Co-ordinator
Sr Research Tech
Sr Research Technol
Senior Scientist
Sr Speech Pathologist
Sr Systems Analyst
Senior Teacher
Senior Technician
Senior Technologist
Sr Telephone Clerk
Sr Urology Tech
Sr Vascular Technol
Server
Service Assistant
Social Worker 1
Social Worker 2
Social Worker 3
Sous Chef
Special Events
  Co-ordinator
Special Project
  Researcher
Specialist
Speech Pathologist
Spinal Cord Program
  Nurse
Sr Pedorthic Tech.
Senior Prosthetist/
  Orthotist
Sr Med Photographer
Staff Chaplain
Staff Epidemiologist

Staff Nurse
Staff RPN
Statistics Assistant 1
Statistics Assistant 2
Steamfitter
Steward
Storeman 1
Storeman 2
Storeman Lead Hand
Student (w Benefits)
Student (wo Benefits)
Supervisor
Surgical Suite Asst
Systems Admin.
Systems Co-ordinator
Systems Programmer
TCAP Officer
Teacher
Teacher's Aide
Teaching Chaplain
Team Leader
Technical Assistant
Technical Service Rep.
Technical Trainer
Technician 1
Technician 2
Technician 3
Technologist 1
Technologist 2
Technologist 3
Technologist 4
Technologist 5
Telephone Operator
Terminal Operator
Trainee Facial Prosthetist
Triage Officer
Tutor
Unit Administrator
Unit Aide
Unit Assistant
Unit Clerk
Urology Technician
User Co-ordinator
Vascular Technologist
Volunteer's Assistant
Waiter/Waitress
Workshop Instructor

This overview of the increasing differentiation in health care cannot leave out furnishers of equipment, drugs, supplies and services to health care providers. Just as there was growing expertise inside health care establishments, the specialised suppliers to them began to develop their own expertise. Drug companies expanded their research establishments outside the hospitals. The surgical-supply salesman learned to perform recondite procedures. Pharmacists and physicians became drug company representatives. There were also new specialist suppliers in areas like hospital maintenance, information systems, and 'hotel services'.

Last but not least, the public, through self-help organisations and disease-advocacy groups, gained highly specific information about treatment patterns, quality of care and technological innovations for many common and rare diseases. The Kidney Foundation, the Arthritis Society and the Diabetes Association have been supplemented by the Myasthenia Gravis Society, the Split Brain Self Help Group, and the Colostomy Association.

This brief and incomplete survey of some differentiation of health care knowledge can give us some sense of the diversity and depth of knowledge that was accumulated. The investments in research and education paid off in vast amounts of highly differentiated knowledge that grew at an accelerating pace. Institutes were created in specialised areas, very often on the model of the old medical superintendent-led hospital. Many health care professionals became the 'medical superintendent' of their own niche specialty. Most were very effective, and highly productive of new knowledge and more effective health care interventions.

As everyone knows:

The greater the differentiation between components of the work, the more need there is for the integration of the entire process. Without such integration, work becomes fragmented with increased risks of gaps, duplications, misunderstandings and mistakes.

The rate of differentiation far exceeded the capacity for integration of this wide range of knowledge and skill, and so health care systems began to consume resources at an accelerating pace, and fragmentation started to occur.

Investment in health care grew. In most countries, the rate of inflation in health care costs was higher than that of general inflation. It was at this time that it began to be clear to economists that health care was supply driven: that is, the more health care services that are provided, the more they will be used. Every new health care service, supply or technology was not accompanied by a reduction of others: most were additive. As each field prospered, it provided more and more useful knowledge. And because each area was so productive, it demanded continuing and even increasing amounts of funding. The old idea that investment in health care research would ultimately reduce health care costs was recognised as a myth – and economists began to fear that expenditure on health care could go out of control.

The end of the 'Good Old Days': inflation makes stronger enclaves

The oil crisis in the 1970s with its accompanying hyper-inflation issued an early warning that there might be limits to the amount of funding for health care. Cost-control measures were strengthened in most countries, and even where they were not, there was a growing awareness that something must be done to limit the costs of health care.

These early attempts were to find ways to restrict, control, limit, and even, in some cases, to reduce the costs of health care. There was no large-scale restructuring. Some limited funding to the overall system as in the UK, others clawed back salaries of health care workers, as in Quebec, and still others restricted funding for particular procedures using DRGs as in the US.

One of the consequences of the reduction of health care spending was that the different specialised activities, which until then were located in non-competing niche areas and given their share of an ever-expanding pie, now began to compete for a more limited one. During the 1980s this competition intensified and divisions which had already begun in the highly differentiated world of health care became epidemic.

The holders of highly specialised knowledge knew the utter importance of that knowledge. If they were clinicians, they knew exactly who could be cured by it, and who was at risk if their knowledge were not put to good clinical use. When the money was not forthcoming, they were prepared to fight for their domain.Now the differentiation which had added to the overall knowledge became dangerously fragmented.

The Hospital's Apple Orchard 1985

The old medical superintendent is now dead. The Ham Green Hospital in Bristol is managed by the Unit General Manager, Richard James, who reports to the District General Manager. Apple crumble is still on the menu and the first taste is a tradition carried on by the Chairman of the Medical Advisory Committee.

The Director of the District Estates Department is in charge of the orchard which remains very productive, but picking the apples costs quite a lot of money and because his budget is constantly being cut, he wants some return for his expenditure. He mentions to the head of catering in the hospital that he really should not expect to continue to get his apples free. The head of catering agrees. He would be willing to pay a fair price for the apples.

The Director of Estates reckons the costs of caring for the orchard. Although the expensive equipment was purchased during the 'Good Old Days', it still

cont.

cont.

must be depreciated, stored, and maintained. There is also the pay for the grounds keepers who pick apples after other work is done and so must be paid at overtime rates. The bill is presented and the head of catering replies that these apples are the most expensive he has seen for a long time and refuses to buy them. He will get his apples from the market.

The apples rot on the tree and the ground. The orchard begins to smell. Insects abound. No one steals the apples because they know that they will be sacked if they are caught. Richard James cannot resolve the dispute because the Director of Estates reports to the District General Manager, while the catering manager reports to him. His entreaties lead the Director of Estates to come up with a resolution of the difficulty: he will cut down the orchard.

The catering staff and the nurses tie themselves to the trees. Richard James declares an amnesty for all those who want to steal apples.

Such fragmentation occurred in many areas of health care, and there were many factors that led to it. We have stressed the increase in effective specialised health care knowledge and technical capacity as well as the funding constraints. But there were many other factors and it is hard to prove which have been the most critical. Some would argue that the complexity of health care is demonstrated by the difficulty in unravelling this kind of problem. But there is no doubt about the phenomenon itself. Fragmentation stories abound. Here are a few recent ones.

Light Bulb Fragments

Jokes about the simple task of screwing light bulbs into their sockets, may not be so funny. Particularly in hospitals, where it typically takes six staff 17 different actions to change a bulb.

The administration for replacing a burnt light takes approximately 20 minutes for each bulb. Multiply this by the number of bulbs in an average hospital and the cost and time equals that of major surgery.

Another example of taxpayers' money disappearing into the realms of inane oblivion, is that it took some hospitals 127 minutes to produce one X-ray, of which only 23 minutes was spent in taking and recording the picture.

The number of administrators in the health service should be cut, rather than the amount of drugs given to patients, says Dr John Griffin, director of the Association of the British Pharmaceutical Industry.

paraphrased from 'Joke Comes True for Hospital Light Bulbs'
by Alan Hamilton
The London Times
Thursday, 30 September 1993

Hospital Politics Split Care

Reggie Lewis, basketball player for the Boston Celtics, collapsed during a playoff game on 29 April 1993. He was brought into the New England Baptist Hospital where a team of cardiologists diagnosed him with cardiomyopathy, 'a potentially life-threatening disease of the heart muscle'.

His doctors thought it would be dangerous for him to change hospitals but they were overruled by the team doctors. Three days after he collapsed, his personal doctors moved him to Brigham and Women's Hospital, where he was diagnosed with a minor fainting condition. Twelve weeks later Reggie Lewis died. An autopsy found that he had a large extensively scarred heart.

According to the *International Herald Tribune*, 'The abrupt switch of hospitals went against normal medical practice, but took place because of the lucrative nature of the cardiology field, the attention on Lewis' case, and the politics within Boston hospitals. 'Boston is the most political medical place in the country,' a cardiologist said. 'There's so many hospitals and so many competitive situations and so much in the way of ego. It had a major influence on this situation.'

paraphrased from 'Celtic Star Hid Heart Murmur'
The Associated Press, *International Herald Tribune*
Boston, Tuesday, 14 September 1993

The spur to reform often came from the fact that any limit on costs resulted in further fragmentation in the system. The decision to reform the UK system thus had an underlying theme of trying to get more and better health care for less money. But the moment to institute it came from a stated lack of paediatric cardiac surgical ICU nursing staff in Birmingham that resulted in the death of a child. This was ascribed to lack of budget, but it remains unclear how much this was due to the fragmentation of care into warring camps of providers struggling over diminished health care funding.

In the US, the pressure for reform was to some extent about an insurance-based system which left 37 million people without any health care coverage at all. The attempts to control the cost of coverage had resulted in fragmented insurance schemes, which provided only partial coverage to those who had insurance. The fragmentation of care was mirrored in the fragmentation of coverage. It resulted in enormous discrepancies between care for the rich and care for the poor.

Fame Brings Extended Life (1995)

In the American health system, almost 30 per cent of the nation's entire Medicare budget is spent during patients' last year of life. Mickey Mantle's doctors decided to give him a liver transplant at the age of 63, because they believed there was a 55 per cent chance of Mantle surviving three more years.

The hospital fee for 11 days before the operation was $32,500 (not including doctors' fees), for assessment of his condition and for cancer tests. The results were negative and it wasn't until the operation that doctors noticed that the cancer had spread dramatically leaving Mantle only a few weeks or at most, a couple of months to live. Had they been aware of the advanced stage of the cancer, the doctors say they wouldn't have operated.

Instead, $20,000 was spent to buy a fresh human liver, plus another $5,000 or more for the chartered plane. Mantle spent two days in intensive care, probably costing several times the usual $1,000 a day or more that hospitals charge, then another 18 days in the hospital. With anti-rejection drugs and other medication running well into five figures, the hospital bill rose by another $116,000. More tests, drugs, and a return to the hospital followed.

Mantle chose to die in a standard hospital room, virtually free of tubes and wires so the total hospital charge therefore stayed under $200,000. But separate bills for surgeons, pathologists, radiologists, oncologists, and gastroenterologists probably equalled the hospital expenses, said Michael Murphy, a health care consultant.

Although it is unclear who paid (Mantle could afford it), the cost of keeping Mickey Mantle alive for two and a half months probably exceeded $300,000.

paraphrased from 'Mantle's Last Medical Bills'
by Allen R Myerson
The New York Times
Sunday, 20 August 1995

Twenty Dollars Proves to Be Too Much (1973)

Mr Tillery who lives alone, had a complete laryngectomy at the age of 56. He was left unable to speak. Just over two weeks after the operation, Mr Tillery was sent home from the hospital. He was given a list of specific equipment necessary for his care: namely, a humidifier and a tracheal suction. Given a list of agencies where he could find the equipment, Mr Tillery was only able to acquire a humidifier, and not a very effective one at that. The suction, he was told, would have to be rented at a cost of $20 a month.

cont.

cont.

Not two days later, Mr Tillery, unable to breathe, woke a neighbour and was sent to emergency. Financially, Mr Tillery did not have much in the way of savings, only enough to last him two or three months, and the $20 necessary to rent the equipment was too much for his stretched budget which already included doctors' bills.

Mr Tillery almost died because of a lack of proper equipment which would have cost $20 a month to rent.

paraphrased from *In Critical Condition:*
The Crisis in America's Health Care
by Edward M Kennedy
New York, Pocket Books, 1973

Just as the driving force of reform was cost reduction, it was almost always the case that the remedy was an attempt to defragment the delivery of care in some way. The efforts addressed different components of health care by restructuring roles, institutions or systems. Many of the papers written for the seminar present these reforms and attempt to assess the results. We have sorted the papers to reflect the nature of the reforms and to display the different views about the reforms and their effects. Broadly speaking there are four major changes that are introduced in the reform mechanisms:

- Centralisation and decentralisation.

- Changes in the public–private mix.

- Managed care.

- Primary and community care focus.

Should health care organisations be centralised or decentralised?

In some countries, there is a strong tendency to decentralise health services. In others there is an equal inclination to centralise them. In the UK, the reforms decentralised organisations into self-governing trusts, while in Canada there has been a move to merge self-governing organisations into larger regions. Ken Jarrold and Don Schurman consider some of the more difficult consequences of these trends.

Minding our own business

❧ *Ken Jarrold* ❧

➤ Editor's comment

In Britain, reforms have devolved the responsibility for individual organisations. Trusts have been created which, though owned by the NHS, have their own boards of trustees (whose members are non-executive directors). These trusts have much greater control over their own destinies than they had as units of larger districts and regions. It was felt that their increased autonomy would make these organisations more responsible for their futures. Their staffs have better relationships with identifiable institutions than with murky districts or arbitrary regions. The creation of trusts would also distinguish the provider hospital from the purchaser who could now look to several different providers for service. This would encourage them to compete with other independent organisations by providing better, or cheaper, or more accessible services.

In his paper, Ken Jarrold urges the managers of individual trusts to work towards a more unified NHS. His paper stresses that managers must assume more responsibility for overcoming some of the negative consequences of the reforms. He begins by pointing out some of the consequences of the creation of trusts. Some have become self-deluding enclaves with an unfounded belief in their own superiority. In others, the managers place local loyalty above loyalty to the larger NHS. And finally, the providers see the purchasers as their adversaries and treat them accordingly.

He believes that inside institutions, the relationship between clinicians and managers has not improved. The introduction of general management in 1984 and the more recent establishment of trusts has not resulted in a more collaborative environment. A study of four trusts indicates some of the increasing distance between nurses and managers. He believes that managers must take a leading role in improving these relations.

In this paper I want to set out two topics for discussion. Firstly, the need for managers in the NHS to care for the NHS, and secondly, the need to work for one NHS because an NHS divided against itself cannot stand.

I want to focus on two 'divides' in the NHS. The first is the purchaser/provider split. The second is the divide between managers and other health service staff. This paper says a little about the first and a great deal about the second. The distribution of time and attention indicates that I believe the staff/managerial gulf is profound and long-lasting and of much greater significance than recently introduced organisational boundaries.

The purchaser/provider split

It is too early to be certain, however I believe that the introduction of the purchaser and provider roles are potentially of great benefit to the NHS. **Health Authorities,** freed from the responsibility for operational management, are beginning to speak for health and for their communities. The most advanced purchasers, and I have had the privilege of working with some of them, are beginning to show what can be done when a Health Authority focuses on the health of its people: defines health strategies and objectives to meet the people's needs; builds healthy alliances with a wide range of partners; and mobilises health, social services, housing and education, statutory and voluntary agencies. When all of this is done, results are delivered for individuals and communities.

Providers can at last develop effective management at the operational level and create a clear identity for their organisation and services in the local community. Devolution of authority to the local level offers potential benefits in terms of speed, effectiveness, relevance, flexibility, and commitment.

If all this is true – why the concern? The concern arises from the fact that every human endeavour offers the potential for progress and for problems. The purchaser/provider split is no exception. Just as there are potential benefits, there are potential problems. Significant among these problems is fragmentation. It is important to guard against the isolationist tendencies of some providers, those of the view that says 'nothing matters to us except the organisation we work in' and that 'we have nothing to learn from the NHS as a whole'.

It is time to reassert the values of the NHS – to say what we stand for – to be open about our beliefs and our commitment. To define what it means to be part of the NHS. Let me give three practical examples of concerns and solutions.

Firstly, I am deeply concerned about those working in health care organisations who believe that they have nothing to learn from others – that nothing is done better anywhere else, and whose mind set is built on bullshit. We need to move from bullshit to learning. We need to listen to Don Berwick who said in his NAHAT speech:

It is important that a learning environment for work be established where it is safe to admit that you do not yet know. Again, comparing the UK to the US, I think it may be a little more difficult here, especially for a person in authority, to say 'I have no idea, I don't know yet'. The position of learner is a position of vulnerability and that is what we need. To willingly place ourselves in the vulnerable position of saying 'I do not know how to do this but I have a way to find out'. Improvement begins with change and change begins with curiosity and so nurtures an environment in which it is safe to say 'I don't know, let's find out'.

I would add that it is not just individuals who need to place themselves willingly in the vulnerable position of saying 'I do not know'. Whole organisations need to develop this and organisations that develop this culture will be whole. It is for this reason that the NHS Executive is establishing a new approach to Personal and Organisational Development – built on the concepts of networking, mentoring and sharing good practice. All the regional offices will be appointing facilitators to take forward this new approach.

Secondly, I am concerned about health care organisations that stress the loyalty of their staff to the point where applications for jobs in other parts of the NHS are regarded as acts of betrayal. This must stop and stop quickly. It is vital for the well being of the NHS – and of the people within it – that we promote movement between the NHS Executive, purchasers, providers, and primary care. We need to develop career planning, not undermine it. We will be developing a number of initiatives including a framework for personal and organisational development and a new approach to ensuring the supply of senior managers based on a top management programme designed by and for the NHS. We also need to spell out expected behaviour so that everyone understands how the NHS regards career planning and the movement of staff. I very much hope that the new Human Resources network for non-executives will provide a forum in which these vital issues can be shared and taken forward.

My third practical point is the framework for relationships between purchasers and providers. As both purchasers and providers mature, we are beginning to be able to look beyond confrontation, outbursts of macho management, annual set-piece duels – to an NHS in which effective purchasing and providing are both founded on long-term strategic relationships which involve key stakeholders including patients, our partners, and the professions. Of course there have to be hard-headed negotiations, of course the issues are complex and demanding, of course it is difficult to reconcile demand, aspirations, efficiency targets and resources – however all of this will make at least a little more sense if purchasers and providers learn to build long-term relationships that identify medium- and long-term shared goals – shared with all those involved.

So much for the purchaser/provider separation. It is an issue. We must overcome the negative effects of the split. We must be one NHS.

The manager/staff divide

I warned you that I would say more about the second of the two divides – that between managers and staff. Let me begin by making it clear that I understand that the staff/manager interface is necessarily a difficult one and that there are natural and even healthy tensions between the two groups. Many NHS staff are trained to focus on the individual and the patient or client group and to do their best for those in need. The managers have a duty to deliver government policy, to ensure cost control and good use of resources. This relationship will never be without its problems.

The issue for me is whether recent events in the NHS have made it more or less difficult to manage this relationship. We need to be concerned about the divide between managers and staff that is developing in the NHS. Unless we respond to this challenge, I fear that it will become dysfunctional.

One of the positive aspects of my job as Director of Human Resources for the NHS Executive is that I have the opportunity to visit health care organisations all over England. One of the strongest impressions that I have is that I am visiting two National Health Services not one. Everywhere I go the senior people – chairs, non-executives, senior managers and even the clinicians most involved in management – tell me of progress, of better working methods and value for money, of objectives achieved, of change delivered. Everywhere I go I glimpse another world, a world inhabited apparently by everyone else – a world of daily crisis and concern, of staff under pressure, and services struggling to deliver. Both worlds are real in the minds of those who inhabit them. Both worlds are supported by objective evidence. Both views are held sincerely.

Crucially for the relationship between the NHS and the community, it is the second world which is always seen on television and in the press. How is it that these two worlds have been created and are so real? I want to trace the events of recent years, to try to understand what has happened and to offer some thoughts about what might be done:

- the coming of a national agenda and a review system to make it stick;
- the arrival of general management;
- the NHS reforms.

National agenda

Until the late seventies, and indeed into the early eighties, no serious attempt was made to define or implement a national agenda for the NHS. Countless circulars were issued and there were a great many policies. However, there were no planning guidelines, no targets, no league tables and no performance management.

It is my clear recollection that from the time I joined the NHS in 1969 until the early eighties, there was a great deal of freedom at the local level. If a senior administrator kept out of financial trouble, avoided scandal and did not upset backbenchers there was little prospect of his or her world being invaded. There were of course, considerable drawbacks with this system: many policies were never implemented and there were enormous variations in resource utilisation and service provision. However, it is easy to see that this was an environment in which the relationship between health service staff and managers was likely to be close. If the manager is not required to implement a national agenda, not called to account by performance management, he or she is far more likely to be guided by local priorities and local views and far less likely to feel inclined to upset the local status quo.

Since the early 1980s we have seen the growth of the national agenda and of strong performance management. Managers at local level now are required to deliver the national agenda. Local issues that stand in the way of delivering national objectives have to be tackled. Managers have to challenge the way in which things have been done. Managers have become identified firmly with the national agenda and with performance management and are seen to be responding to national pressures rather than local views.

General management

The second aspect that I want to discuss is the arrival of general management. In 1983, I took part in a debate and opposed a motion supporting the appointment of Chief Executives in the NHS. I now believe that I was wrong to do so. I would now argue that general management and the appointment of Chief Executives have strengthened the management process and personal accountability in the NHS. Indeed, I wonder if the NHS would have coped with the challenges of the last 11 years without the introduction of general management. However, it may be interesting to know why I opposed the motion and what relevance it has to the theme of this paper.

I argued that Chief Executives were inappropriate because of the power of individual professionals based on clinical freedom and a personal responsibility to patients, because of the complex pattern of relationships between professions and because of the lengthy process of consultation inside and outside the service. I said that our great challenge was to 'persuade those who have the power in the service to share the responsibility' and I forecast that the professions would 'retreat delightedly from whatever degree of responsibility they have accepted and place this burden on the Chief Executive'. In one of my few perceptive moments, I drew attention to the temptation there would be to treat the Chief Executive as a scapegoat. How easy it would seem to change the Chief Executive instead of solving the problems!

However, that was all a long time ago and no one took any notice anyway. Just as well because, as I have already conceded, I was wrong. However, I may have been partly right in the diagnosis even if I was wrong in the recommended treatment. I understood the nature of the NHS. A complex mix of nearly 40 occupational groups including very powerful professions. This environment had been administered largely on the basis of consent and team decisions. There had been towering figures – able administrators who had ruled their Boards of Governors and Hospital Management Committees with rods of iron. However, on the whole, they had built their power and influence on personal ability and credibility. General Management changed all that. Formal consensus terms disappeared and everywhere Chief Executives were appointed and invested with considerable power. It was a tremendous shock to the culture of the NHS. A shock from which some health service staff still have not recovered.

NHS reforms

The third aspect of recent events that has a bearing on my theme is the NHS reforms. Since *Working for Patients* was published in 1989, the NHS has experienced the most radical changes in its history. Almost every aspect of the reform has been highly controversial. It is difficult to remember the vehemence with which the reforms were opposed. NHS Trusts were said to be the end of civilisation as we knew it – GP Fundholding was the end of general practice and no GP would ever apply for such a terrible scheme! In the middle of all this controversy, one thing was clear. It was the managers who were to be responsible for implementing the reforms. It was the managers who were seen to benefit. It was the managers who became closely associated with these policies.

Of course the three items are interconnected. General Management made the review process more effective and made it much easier to hold the NHS to account for the national agenda. The reforms would have been very difficult, if not impossible to implement without general management. The national agenda and the review system, general management and the reforms have worked together to separate managers from the rest of the staff of the health service.

And of course, along the way we have had short-term contracts, performance-related pay, substantial salary increases, controversial severance payments, and lease cars.

It is important to remember that all these events have been played out against a background of resource constraints and pressures. Managers have had the responsibility of coping with resource constraints, increasing demand, rising expectations and ever more demanding national policies, standards and targets. All of this has made it inevitable that managers would have to challenge accepted practice and vested interests. To implement unpopular service reviews, to close wards and indeed hospitals, to question staffing levels and patterns.

Is it surprising that after all these changes there should be a divide between managers and other health service staff?

Before I refer to one piece of evidence to support my concerns, I want to make clear that I am not being wholly critical of NHS managers. Of course there is bad management; of course some of the changes have been introduced insensitively; of course there has been macho management. However, I believe that the vast majority of NHS managers have tried conscientiously to do their job, often in very difficult circumstances. They are dealing with one of the most difficult managerial agendas in the world. I am proud to be one of them.

And so to the evidence. In the course of preparing this paper, I tried to find reliable evidence of the nature of the relationship between managers and staff. I found an article in the recent edition of the *Journal of Advanced Nursing* by Michael Traynor, a Research Officer with the Daphne Heald Research Unit at the Royal College of Nursing. Michael Traynor studied the impact, over three years, of the 1987 primary care reforms (Promoting Better Health), 'Caring for People and Working for Patients' on the organisation and morale of community nurses. The research was undertaken in four first-wave trusts. Interestingly the management of one trust withdrew from the study after receiving the result of the first year survey! Nine hundred and ninety nurses were involved and managers were also interviewed. The difference in perceptions between nurses and managers was great indeed. Let me give you a flavour of the results:

Nurses generally appeared to feel alienated from the world and values of their managers, particularly senior management.

Many nurses clearly saw management as too theoretical and out of touch with the daily realities of trying to provide care in increasingly difficult circumstances.

Managers were seen as being concerned with profit and loss – 'Money is god and clerical work second' – with saving money and getting a good name for themselves, with posh offices and statistics.

Managers were seen as highly qualified but indecisive and too aloof. Managers were seen as having 'thoughtful eyes' in contrast with the 'common-sense hands' of the nurses.

Many practitioners felt that not only did managers not share their philosophy of care, but that they had no understanding of the complexity the issues involved or the sheer volume of their work. This, coupled with the knowledge that managers have power (to grant or withdraw resources) led many nurses to feel insecure if they believed that their work was not understood or valued.

It would be easy to dismiss all this as the understandable response of a conservative profession being challenged by resource constraint. Indeed the managers had a few views of their own! They saw nurses as traditionalists, as having limited perspective, as fearful, and even as headless chickens! Nurses were seen as nurse-centred rather than patient-centred.

Even though this is only one piece of evidence, even if we can all rationalise the results, I believe that the result would be repeated in many other places and in many other groups of health service staff. I believe that we have a real problem. Nearly 20 years of radical reform, strengthened managerial grip, and resource pressures, have produced a divide between health service staff and the managers.

I promised to end with some thoughts about what might be done. Let me make it clear that I am realistic about what *can* be done. I do not believe that the clock can be put back to the 'good old days'. Whoever is in power, whatever the trend of government policy, many of the realities will endure. The resource pressures will not go away, governments are unlikely to abandon a national agenda or performance management, and we can say with certainty that cash limiting will remain in place. Whatever aspects of the NHS reforms might be reversed by a government of a different party, I would be very surprised if general management were overturned in favour of consensus teams.

What can be done? Something can and must be done: improving standards of management. We need to support and develop managers at all levels to help them to cope with the enormous challenges they face. Competent managers, secure in their skill and experience, are more likely to handle change in a sensitive way and less likely to indulge in aggressive management. If managers are to be expected to increase the efficiency and effectiveness of the NHS, we must not forget to support and develop these managers and to increase their efficiency and effectiveness.

However, I believe that this is only part of the solution. The main requirement, in my view, is to make clear to the NHS the managerial behaviour that is required: that which is most likely to reduce the divide between health service staff and managers.

I believe that both individuals and organisations respond rapidly to messages. The messages of the last few years have been about management changes, reforms, and the delivery of bottom lines. All that has been necessary and right. However, we now need to send a new message to managers in the NHS. We cannot change the current message but we can add to it. We cannot remove the need for managers to deliver the bottom lines, to maintain financial discipline, to deliver national objectives and targets. However we can say that this, however difficult it may be, is not enough. If we are to halt the widening of the divide between staff and managers, and perhaps even narrow the divide, then we must say that we will value those managers who deliver the bottom lines and who are knowledgeable about, demonstrate interest in, and care for the work. Managers must show staff that they have a genuine knowledge of and interest in the 'business' of the NHS – patient care.

Kotter in his outstanding book on General Managers comes to the following conclusion:

The most effective General Managers had careers characterised by almost constant

*growth in their interpersonal and intellectual skills, in their knowledge of the business
and the organisation and in their relationship with relevant others.*

The phrase that I want to emphasise is 'in their knowledge of the business and the
organisation'. It is this that leads Kotter to recommend that most large organisations
should seek to grow their own senior managers from within the organisation. I
believe that we must send a new message to managers. We must ask them to
demonstrate clearly their commitment to the NHS and its values, their interest in
and knowledge of patient care, their delight in the richness and variety of
occupational skills and experience, their care for the work of the service and its staff.
And I believe that this behaviour must find practical expression in caring for staff –
in more considerate people management, in staff support including improved
occupational health and counselling services.

Let me make it clear that I don't imagine that in the vast majority of cases we are
going to have to persuade managers or educate managers to behave in this way. The
vast majority of managers believe in this form of managerial behaviour and wish to
practice it in their daily work. A substantial group has maintained this behaviour
despite all the changes and pressures of recent years. What managers need is a
mandate to do what they instinctively want to do. They need the green light that
says this behaviour is OK – it is more than OK – it is what is required. Health service
managers do need to be concerned with more than bottom lines and managerial
change – they do need to demonstrate their commitment to the NHS, their interest
in and knowledge of patient care.

Sir Roy Griffiths understood all this. He pointed out that a successful organisation
needed both a careful strategy and motivated staff – that staff are not motivated by
managerial topics (money and strategies) but by talk of quality and of patient care. He
knew that the first need is for staff to feel confident that their top managers know what
they – the staff – are doing. He said that if we talk to staff and get support from the
professions, a lot of the public perception will follow. Sir Roy's words have real wisdom.

I believe that if we can make clear to the NHS the managerial behaviour required,
we can change managerial behaviour. Managers must reinforce existing staff
commitment to the NHS, and their interest in and knowledge of the work of patient
care. If all this can be achieved, we will see a real change in the attitudes and
motivation of staff. I believe that staff will react very positively to managers who
show that they are not only concerned with bottom lines but with the work – the
business of the NHS. Nothing is more likely to motivate staff than managers who
show that they care about the same things that the staff care about.

And so I return to my propositions: I believe that we must ask NHS managers to
mind our own business. To care for the NHS and to demonstrate that care. I also
believe that we need to work for one NHS because an NHS divided against itself
cannot stand.

The agony and the ecstasy of reform

Donald P Schurman

Editor's comment

Donald Schurman introduces his critique of the Alberta restructuring by declaring that the dramatic increase of knowledge about health and the very rapid introduction of new technology demand that we rethink how we deliver health care. He goes on to describe the success of the restructuring in Oregon and contrasts it with the structural changes that have occurred in Alberta.

In 1994, following the lead of other provinces, Alberta eliminated the boards of 122 individual hospitals and health units and replaced them with 17 regions. The main reason for this regionalisation was to reduce the cost of governance and management. The other objective was to shift resources out of the tertiary care centres to community health networks.

Schurman argues that the changes were imposed by the government with little consultation and without careful analysis of their consequences. The business plans associated with the changes were thus flawed and the manager of one of the major regions resigned because the criticism and pressure were too much. In rural areas the populations have become 'confused and angry at the impact of health reform'.

He concludes that in Alberta, changes in the health care system must relate to our new understanding of health, and not be only financially or politically driven.

This paper has been edited in parts to focus on the comparison between Oregon and Alberta's health care reforms.

Introduction

All torment, trouble, wonder and amazement inhabits here: some heavenly power guide us out of this fearful country!

Gonzalo, *The Tempest*, Act 5, Scene 1, ln. 104

T he practice of medicine stands on the verge of a revolution based on new knowledge of the ways in which inherited genetic risk factors[1] contribute to the health of individuals. This paper is based on a presumption that we are living through a fundamental shift in health care knowledge which will dramatically alter the way in which care can be delivered, and challenge how we manage the system that delivers care.

My starting point for this discussion is that we may already have entered new territory, and that old ways of managing and doing business will not bring success. To illuminate the basic thread of my argument, I will look at both the Oregon Health Services Plan experiment and Alberta's implementation of Regional Health Authority governance and management structure, in the manner of a case study of broad organisational change designed to contribute to the creation of a new health care delivery system. Most of the case study material will deal with the Alberta experiment, as that is the situation with which I am most familiar.

Today, medicine, and health care generally, is becoming an increasingly global phenomenon. The personal computer, fibre-optics and the Internet have changed this context, and contributed to the breaking-down of barriers between specialties, disciplines and health care delivery systems. The application of information technology raises the possibility of providing broad public access to medical information and information about what works and how it works. In short, the paradigm used by those within the industry to manage the health care system is being challenged and changed in ways that we see only dimly at this time.

If information is not understood and shared, then appropriate responses are not possible. Conversations break down. Effective outcomes may not be achieved, and the successful organisation of a delivery system based on a new partnership between those who have knowledge and those who need to have access to that knowledge, may become virtually impossible.

Each party in a conversation bears responsibility for actively listening, understanding, and fulfilling any commitments. In the future, new information will lead to new accountabilities and require different responsibilities between practitioners and clients. Future health delivery systems will need to be designed to allow meaningful dialogues to occur, and positive outcomes to result. There are two fundamental questions inherent in this: 'What knowledge is implemented and appropriately utilised to ensure a good outcome?' and, 'How should the activity leading to good outcomes be structured as a delivery system?'.

Patients or clients rarely read or care about mission statements, visions, or strategic plans. Users of the health system and its component parts want their or their family-members' problems handled quickly and with compassion. A person receiving care for their kidney stone problem probably doesn't worry about or care whether or not the heart bypass operation occurring on the floor above leads to a good outcome or to death.

Physicians have their own particular view of what makes for an ideal system. The trouble is that, apart from a few general features, there is a great deal of variation in their view of what makes for a good health care delivery system. Nephrologists dealing with waiting lists for dialysis or kidney transplants do not particularly concern themselves with the challenges faced by a family physician having to deal with the consequences of family violence.

Oregon

The Oregon Health Services experiment is one well-known attempt to create change and manage health care services in a new way. While the popular interpretation has relied on the rationing aspect of the Oregon Health Plan, Oregon's health reform process was based on a broad consultative approach designed to create an active listening situation between providers, who were asked to provide the medical facts, and the public, who were asked the value of various health states[2]. Useful lessons can be drawn from understanding how the dialogue was developed:

❏ In the early 1980s, a non-profit community action group, called Oregon Health Decisions asked the Oregon public to establish values related to health.

❏ In 1988, a citizen's parliament was held to provide the legislature with information about goals and direction.

❏ In 1989, an Oregon Health Services Commission took on the work which lead to the Oregon Health Plan.

Oregon learned four important lessons from its initiative:

❏ The first lesson was that the community had to acknowledge and understand that while health care needs were infinite, the resources to meet these needs were finite. This meant that initial work had to be directed at differentiating the public's needs from its wants.

❏ The second lesson was to realise how essential public involvement was and to design processes for getting their involvement. The public's involvement should not be treated paternalistically. The experience in Oregon was that the public knew its desires regarding health status and was community-minded in relation to the overall health of the population.

❏ The third lesson was that accurate and user-friendly information does not exist in health care. This admission is startling given that many current reform efforts focus on developing information related to outcomes and care. If it does not exist, then we need to consider competing hypotheses that such information was never needed, that we come from a culture which does not want to produce user-friendly information, or that we were not capable of capturing the information required.

❑ The fourth lesson was that the vision of reform would be over-arching. Oregon achieved success by avoiding dogmatic ownership of a methodology and focusing on achieving their goal.

Was the Oregon experiment a fluke? Can it serve as a model for how to engage the public in a broad debate about what constitutes health and what is the best way to organise scarce resources to meet health needs? Answers will not be available until someone else tries to replicate the experience. What cannot be disputed is that this sort of dramatic change, involving a field of social interest like the health care system, requires a tremendous commitment to involving the community in the discussion, design, and delivery of health services.

What the Oregon experience indicates is that the listening process first started with a conversation initiated in the broader community. This conversation was heard by politicians who then established a more formal process for engaging in a broad dialogue with the population of the state. The goal was ensuring a basic level of access and service within a limited budget. The process chosen was designed to allow understanding to build and was one which engaged physicians and health professionals at major decision points. It used a format – local town hall meetings – rooted deep within American political culture.

Alberta

Alberta chose a different route from that of Oregon. In July 1993, Alberta's provincial Progressive Conservative party was re-elected with a mandate to eliminate the province's annual average deficit of $2.1 billion, and the accumulated provincial debt of $20 billion which had been acquired over six years. It was clear that this sort of action required major expenditure reductions for health services, which were approximately 30 per cent of total annual provincial expenditures.

As this direction was being finalised and set, the entire apparatus of government was being shifted to a results-based management focus heavily influenced by the work of Sir Roger Douglas in New Zealand, and of Gabler and Osborne in America.

The financial goal of Alberta's health reform was to reduce health care spending by $745 million (17.5 per cent) within four years, by 1997. The service goal was the re-orientation of the delivery system away from a disease model to a wellness model focused on community-based care. This change would require hospital capacity to be reduced, community-based care to be increased, and the incomes of health care workers to be reduced. The major strategy for accomplishing these changes would be the creation of regional health authorities with complete authority over the funding and delivery of health services for a defined population.

The change process began with an invited round table on health care change which was held in the autumn of 1993. This was followed by an unprecedented series of town hall meetings throughout Alberta which culminated in the government issuing a major white paper on health care policy, 'Starting Points: Recommendations for Creating a More Accountable and Affordable Health System', in December 1993.

This policy white paper was a watershed for Alberta. Seventeen regional health authorities were established, each with an average of fifteen members. The governance framework was established in legislation with the promulgation of the Regional Health Authorities Act. These authorities were given full operational responsibility and accountability for the funding and delivery of health services to the population in their area. These government-appointed bodies replaced hospital and public health bodies throughout Alberta. The main selling point behind the change was the reduction of waste and duplication through the elimination of the administrative overhead represented by 122 hospitals and health unit boards, and the consolidation and elimination of administrative staff.

Unlike the Oregon Health Experiment, the Alberta challenge was not how to extend a minimal level of coverage and service. The Alberta challenge was to reduce operating costs and capacity and to re-focus the remaining elements to prevention and community-based health care.

There was no flexibility in meeting the pressure to reduce capacity, as the government had specified funding-reduction targets designed to meet its overall fiscal objective of a balanced budget by 1997. Within days of their appointment, the major focus for Regional Health Authority boards was the production of a business plan within three months, specifying how they would meet the government's three-year deficit reduction goals. This work was to take place between July and September, 1994.

This work was to be done without the regional health authorities having any staff of their own, and without their taking official control of any of the facilities or services in the region until February or March 1995 – months away.

With the exception of one physician who was appointed in a remote part of the province, physicians as a group were excluded from membership on the first regional health authorities. This effectively barred them from being privy and partner to significant discussions regarding the reduction of hospital beds, the closure of hospitals in some areas and the development of policies designed to reduce dramatically lengths of stay in hospital. While these decisions were made, there existed a *de facto* responsibility for physicians to ensure that the quality of care did not decline or become otherwise compromised.

Early on in the process of realigning the hospital system, it became necessary to re-examine the whole role of medical privileges and hospital medical staffs. In one region, the Capital Health Authority which governed Edmonton, a document was prepared which outlined a radical new approach to privileging, and which suggested that physicians would become obligated to enter into one-year contracts with the local authority. If, during the year, certain conditions were not satisfied, the Capital Health Authority would reserve the right not to renew the contract.

This discussion document and the physicians' views that they were not adequately involved with the decision-making structure led to a gathering of 900 physicians at which the local health board and their executive staff were shouted at and otherwise abused. The meeting was absolutely unprecedented in the history of physician-board relations in Alberta. Since that meeting in Edmonton, a similar meeting took place in Calgary, though it appeared to lack the emotional fervour associated with the Edmonton meeting.

The business plans that were produced had problems. All regional health authorities had received instructions in the preparation of business plans at a three-day retreat with government bureaucrats. Membership on many authorities was drawn from the business community which should have meant a familiarity with business planning was built into the governance structure. Each Regional Health Authority business plan was designed to meet the restructuring challenge for the residents in its area.

The breadth of consultation varied widely. In one Northwest region, the regional Health Authority visited every community and reviewed a broad range of service data. The members of this regional authority understood that major health challenges facing the local aboriginal community had not been served well by the care systems of the past. They broke with standard planning and embarked on the creation of aboriginal healing centres designed to address these problems. They committed to consultation with native elders and the preparation of a plan which aligned and reflected the values of each native community in the area.

From the Capital Health Region Board, which had major tertiary care responsibilities for Northern and Central Alberta as well as responsibility for designated provincial programmes such as organ transplantation, one board member was heard to express pride in the fact their business plan had been completed without any significant consultation. The business plan, prepared by the Capital Health Authority, was prepared within the three-month allotted time limit and addressed a plan for meeting the government's fiscal goals.

A health economist, reviewing the business plan prepared by the Capital Health Authority, questioned several key assumptions contained in the report. The business plan document listed as a fact that the average length of stay in Edmonton hospitals was one day longer than the average for the rest of Alberta and that Alberta's length of stay was 2.2 days over the national average. The analysis by the health economist, which appeared in the local newspaper, concluded that the Capital Health Authority's analysis was out in its Alberta estimate by about 30 per cent, and their error for their home region, Edmonton, was out by about 40 per cent. In the opinion of the university-based analyst reviewing these estimates, the Capital Health Authority would not be able to achieve their spending targets for acute care hospitals without imposing hardships on the people in the region.

Other questions were directed at the accuracy of the only table in the business plan that summarised the Capital Health Authority's allocation and reallocation of resources from the tertiary referral system to the community health centres. According to the business plan, three major tertiary care hospitals were to come together into what was called a specialty referral hospital network. Three smaller hospitals were to be the core of what was being termed community health networks. These networks were to serve the primary care and minor surgery needs of the population, and be a focus at the community level for disease prevention and health promotion activity. The funding for high technology, tertiary services was to fall from $660 million in 1994–5 to $292 million by 1996–7 – a decrease of 56 per cent. The funding for the community health networks was planned to increase from $32 million in 1994–5 to $291 million by 1996–7 – a swingeing increase.[3]

Such dollar shifts clearly indicate a major transformation in role and responsibility for two main tertiary facilities such as the Royal Alexandra and University of Alberta Hospitals, the principal referral centres. Each hospital has a prime trauma programme and heart surgery programme, and the University Hospital provides regional dialysis and transplant programmes. Both hospitals offer a broad array of high-technology programmes which have a teaching and research component. When it is considered that, during fiscal year 1993–4, the University Hospital's total expenditure was $299 million – $7 million more than was planned on being spent by the Capital Health Authority board for three tertiary care referral centres at the end of 1997 – then the financial figures in the Capital Health Authority's business plan become unbelievable.

While much of the shift in resources noted in the business plan could have reflected simple changes in accounting practices and assigning cost centres differently, this is not the essence of health reform. Shifting cost centres from one heading to another does not reform processes of care and does not engage the community in a dialogue about what constitutes health.

At the time of this writing, there are further indications that Alberta's regional health reforms are becoming problematic. The Chief Executive Officer of the Calgary Regional Health Authority just recently resigned citing lack of time for activity away from the job, and constant criticism and pressure as contributing factors. Throughout rural Alberta, communities facing hospital closures or hospital role reallocation are becoming confused and angry at the impact of health reform. In some rural areas, closure of the hospital is leading to the loss of their primary care physicians, further complicating an already difficult readjustment.

Learning lessons

The Oregon and Alberta experiments are two quite different attempts at health reform. At face value, they appear so different that any comparison of them might be considered inappropriate.

I contend that a major lesson can be learned from a comparison. In the Oregon case, while the public may have had a difficult time understanding the technical complexity of the arguments presented, they were able to understand what they were gaining from the health reforms: basic access to a range of services. The process involved clarifying values, presenting data and dealing with the emotional context of this change.

In the Alberta case, the public had to be involved differently – partly because regional boards were appointed and perceived to be successful government patronage seekers – and it was not at all clear to the public what was being received from health reform, though they appeared to have readily understood what was being lost.

Using business plans, which have to be data-driven, was not a poor idea in itself. But, when the first business plans contain what appear to be factual errors and financial tables which make little or no sense, then the initial false steps caused by this misuse of data yields losses in credibility which are difficult to make up.

The Oregon process was designed to be iterative. Once judgements were made, or a phase was completed, the body or committee in charge of the task went back to the public for a reality check. This allowed flexibility around means without necessarily compromising the consensus which had been built about the goals of the process.

In Alberta, the change process appeared to have the linear quality of a pre-set agenda and no amount of public feedback was being allowed to interfere with the inevitable re-focusing of the delivery system. Although 15,000 residents of Edmonton assembled in a field and protested closure of intensive care services and an increased presence for psychiatric services, the Regional Board remained committed to its overall plan for change.

The Oregon experiment understood that the nature of health reform involved the personal element of health care relations discussed by Relman. The Oregon process was designed to deal with the important aspects of that relationship, namely the values of participants and their emotions about changes in health care services delivery.

The Alberta experiment appeared to understand the structural reforms required to shift care from facilities to the community, but somehow, in the execution, relied on a grass roots approach to involving and creating local control structures which was not appropriately related to the kind of change being implemented.

As soon as reforms like regionalisation are started, two schools of thought come into conflict. On the one hand, some argue that a regional body, representative of the residents of the area, is in the best position to work with the community to decide on health needs and a plan for how to meet those needs. On the other, a regional system is a better way of centrally managing knowledge in the care system. It is a also a good way to create core competencies in various sectors and settings and thus make the best available use of resources.

It is a mistake to assume that these two streams are actually one. They are different and need to be managed differently. Each connects at the governance level of a regional board, but there are different tasks and activities which lead to success.

From the point of view of structural reform, the creation of a regional service delivery structure has to have a proper place for academic medicine at its centre. The proper activities of academic medicine involve high-technology clinical services, education and research. In an era when resources are shrinking and health care is becoming more global, it makes sense to concentrate demand and focus in one centre. As the future unfolds, academic centres will probably assume more important roles as couriers of new knowledge and evaluators of new technology.

Another key element which has to be recognised in attempts at structural reform is that physicians cannot be excluded or even appear to be excluded from the activity of structural reform. As Relman rightly points out, a medical encounter – or for that matter a health encounter – has a personal quality which can never be ignored. Systems need to be aligned with the realities of these encounters. Some measure of inexactitude will be endemic to the patient-practitioner encounter so systems can never be completely integrated or honed to the degree that all error is eliminated. However, physicians have to be involved in designing services which are practical and which can let the practice of medicine unfold in a resource-constrained environment.

Any change planned along the lines pursued in Alberta has to focus on educating the public about how well the current system works as well as how much better a re-tooled system will work. In short, there has to be a strong and concerted effort to identify the value and benefit of the community-based system which is being created. It's not enough to merely say that community health networks will be created. The creation of these networks has to represent a value or demand which the local community desires.

If health administrators, planners and regional board members who embark on a process of structural reform of the delivery system structure merely articulate the carefully guarded truths of their training as a mantra without understanding that building community structures is a long, tough job, then they will not understand why their plans and goals are not adopted by their communities. Changing health care through structural reform cannot be done in a vacuum which ignores the values of participants and their emotional attachment to structures and programmes currently in place.

The Alberta experience suggests that care needs to be exercised over the instruments chosen to encourage change. In retrospect, using business plans as the guiding tools probably fits the fiscal agenda quite well, but they were a terribly poor vehicle for dealing with the values and emotions of change.

Somewhat ironically, Alberta's Regional Health Authorities Act does not speak of business plans at all. It discusses a statutory requirement to deliver a health plan which explains to the population of the region how the Health Authority is to deliver it. Regional Health Authorities had the responsibility for the promotion and protection of the health of the population in the given region, to prevent injury and disease. Very few Health Authority business plans focused on these 'health' tasks, rather choosing to portray the fiscal challenge as the major challenge. This approach made the regional health authorities appear to be bankers or moneylenders.

This is an appropriate place to end our analysis and discussion. Our starting point was Shakespeare's *The Tempest*. Talking of moneylenders and bankers brings to mind another play. Before ending, it might be useful to illustrate how decisions might be made differently in the future.

One of the first major service decisions announced by the Capital Health Authority in Edmonton was the reallocation of the complete obstetrics and gynaecology programme (including gynaecological oncology) of the University Hospital to the Royal Alexandra Hospital site. The Royal Alexandra Hospital and the University Hospital both had obstetrics and delivery programmes which handled high-risk cases. With this decision made, high-risk cases were to be sent to the Royal Alexandra Hospital, and low-risk cases were to be distributed among the three hospitals which were centres to the community health networks.

The decision was not well received, as it included all elements including the research and teaching role. The data used to make the decision relied on average costs and a retrospective analysis of activity. The impact on other services, such as the Neo-natal Intensive Care Service at the University Hospital, was given some consideration but not enough weight to assure front-line staff of the quality of the decision. The public was engaged in the media from an emotional point of view and interviews with parents who had babies delivered at the University Hospital site filled the newspapers and television news programmes.

The public did not seem to have a clear idea of the benefits that would accrue because of this change, even though the work-up to this decision had been under discussion for at least three years prior to this current decision being announced. Benefits arrive in the future, but costs are here today. The debate, as it unfolded, dealt with today's costs and not tomorrow's benefits.

There were resources in the region to assemble a team of physicians, health services researchers and hospital planners to assess the future costs or savings associated with this move, and engage the public in a debate about how the benefits of changing services in this way would translate into expenditure over time. Rather than focusing on the current or historical cost of the service being shifted, an analysis of how high-risk babies delivered at each site actually fared once they had progressed beyond the neonate stage of life could have been undertaken. This analysis might have revealed the outcomes and associated long-term costs that were being incurred from each site. This information could then have been used to determine, or at least suggest, what sort of long-term costs would be incurred over their lifetimes.

With such an analysis, the decision whether or not to consolidate obstetrics and gynaecology in a single site would then have been an investment decision. The Board would have been concerned about the value of its investment and the consequence of making one capital investment as opposed to another. That would have led to a very different conversation between the Board and its community about why the change was needed and what would be accomplished.

When these sorts of study and this kind of information are more widely considered and accepted *before* decisions are taken, then we will know that we are on the way to developing a reformed health system.

Building a delivery system which is focused on creating opportunities for health at both the individual and community level is about our shared future. Ultimately, those of us involved with health reform activity will need to embrace new ways of looking at the business of health care, have the courage to do things differently based on new perspectives about what constitutes value, and dare to share information with our communities in new ways as we work together to create new community-based health delivery systems.

References

1 For a discussion of medical and information systems innovations on the horizon, please see William B Schwartz, 'In the Pipeline: A Wave of Valuable Medical Technology', in *Health Affairs* (Summer 1994) pp70–9. Schwartz provides an excellent overview of developments currently on their way.

2 The information on the Oregon Health experiment is taken from Paige R Sipes-Metzler, 'Health Care Reform in Oregon' in *Leadership in Health Care*, (Vol. 3 No. 3) pp33–6.

3 Capital Health Authority, 'A New Direction for Health', p12.

Should health care be public or private?

A second controversy is about how much health care should be funded from public sources, and how much should be provided by private suppliers. Increased user fees, privatised services, competitive for-profit tendering are examples of some of the changes. Frank Burns describes how the profit motive goes hand in hand with quality improvement. Marie Fortier describes a major Canadian federal review of health care and fears that increasing privatisation of health care will threaten the basic values of the Canadian health care systems.

Reform of the UK National Health Service
So far, so good or thus far and no further?

❦ *Frank Burns* ❧

❦ Editor's comment

Frank Burns is in favour of a commercial model for health care delivery. He approaches the debate by reviewing how the NHS has changed since the reforms began. He evaluates them against their objectives and concludes that privatised providers might best serve NHS interests.

He argues that the NHS has changed dramatically in the last few years. Its structure has altered so that 'virtually every hospital and community care provider is now a semi-autonomous NHS Trust'. Similarly, there will soon be 'fully integrated purchasing/commissioning authorities for populations of up to half a million people'.

The reforms have achieved mixed success. They have not really succeeded in establishing needs or evidence-based priorities for purchasing. Nor have they shifted resources from major hospitals to primary care and community services. But there has been an improvement in the efficiency and quality of services. The reforms are leading to a modification of hospital services, by distributing them in a more logical and effective way.

Burns believes that the reform process is hampered by the fact that the market is not real. 'Both purchasers and providers operate safe in the knowledge that there is a hierarchy to pick up the pieces if they make a mess of things.' Although he thinks it is unlikely to happen, because of the politics, he believes that the best thing to do would be to create a genuinely independent provider sector and to free the purchasers from political constraints. This would accelerate the reform process and NHS purchasers could then contract for NHS care in a 'provider market that is substantially or wholly in the private sector.'

Introduction

At the time of the King's Fund International Seminar in Los Angeles (1991), the UK contingent was (with a couple of exceptions) somewhat demoralised over the then recent introduction of the Conservative government's radical reforms of the National Health Service.

The details of these reforms have been covered at previous seminars and will no doubt be described in other papers. For the purpose of this paper, the key elements of the reforms can be summarised as follows:

❑ The dismantling of a hierarchical allocation process into separate Purchaser and Provider entities.

❑ The creation of Purchasing Authorities with a remit to commission and contract for health services for a defined population within a fixed tax-funded allocation.

❑ The establishment of a mechanism whereby groups of general practitioners could claim their share of the local purchasing allocation and be responsible for contracting directly with providers for a limited range of services for patients on their own lists.

❑ The creation of semi-autonomous health care providers (NHS Trusts) whose survival within the internal market depended on their success in securing contracts to provide services to Purchasing Authorities and General Practitioner fund-holders.

❑ A requirement for health care professionals in general, and doctors in particular, to evaluate the effectiveness of their treatment regimes through an organised process of audit.

As intimated above, the majority of the UK contingent to the 1991 International Conference was hostile to these reforms and amongst many reasons for their opposition, the following were paramount:

- The obvious unpopularity of the reforms amongst the general public.
- Fierce resistance to the reforms from National Health Service staff.
- The potential for market forces to undermine strategic goals.
- The imposition of a prevailing political philosophy into the hugely sensitive health arena.
- The elevation of the NHS to the hottest political issue of the time.
- A loss of personal power associated with the dismantling of the old managerial hierarchy.
- A concern about the damaging impact of radical change on the service.

On the final afternoon of the 1991 meeting, participants met in their national groups to discuss what they had gained from the week that could be of practical value to the debate on health care issues in the respective countries represented.

Not surprisingly, the discussion of the UK contingent was lively throughout, heated in places, and positively bad tempered at times. Present at this discussion was Len Shaeffer, the Chief Executive of Blue Cross California and host for the Conference, who, in a moment of extreme exasperation, made a particularly robust contribution to the discussion which included the following observation:

> *It seems to me that you managers in the UK spend more time defending the National Health Service as a way of providing health care to the exclusion of the more important debate about what can be done to improve the mediocre service which characterises much of the delivery end of the NHS when compared to the 'customer is king' ethos in the USA.*

(After more than four years I don't pretend the above is an exact record of what Len Shaeffer said but it certainly reflects the essence of it.)

In making this point, Len was clearly responding to the passion with which some of the UK contingent were defending the traditional allocation process as a way of achieving health care objectives when faced with the evil of contracts, competition and crass commercialism as exemplified by the inhumanity of a USA health care system which fails to meet the needs of the poor and the uninsured.

Len clearly found it difficult to reconcile the myth of the NHS utopia with the fact that vast numbers of people in the UK were waiting for one, two, and even three years to get an out-patient appointment with a similar range of waiting times before admission. He could equally well have made disparaging references to other failures of the old NHS. In particular, he might have criticised the failure of the service to target resources in accordance with national priorities (primary care, community care, the elderly, the mentally ill, deprived communities, etc.), despite the availability of an organisational structure over the previous 40 years designed to facilitate rational targeting of resources.

The current situation

In the four years since the Los Angeles meeting, the Conservative government has pressed ahead with the implementation of the NHS reform to the extent that virtually every hospital and community-care provider is now a semi-autonomous NHS Trust. Legislation is imminent which will complete the establishment of fully integrated purchasing/commissioning authorities for populations of up to half a million people.

In some areas, up to three-quarters of general practitioners have claimed their share of the local purchasing allocation and are purchasing a limited range of acute and community services for their own patients. In various parts of the country, general practitioner fund-holders are working co-operatively to create more effective and more integrated locality purchasing units for natural communities of up to 60,000 people. This latter trend has been reflected in a recent and major evolution of the reform process in which the government is advocating the devolvement of purchasing and contracting responsibilities to general practitioners. These GPs operate either as fund-holders or members of a locality purchasing consortium, contracting for services, within a policy and priorities framework, agreed with and monitored by the statutory purchasing commissions.

The hostility to reform of the National Health Service, which was central to the discussions of the UK contingent at the 1991 meeting, reflects very well the unrelenting controversy and opposition in the country as a whole to this most fundamental series of reforms to what, after all, is one of the most cherished of the UK's national institutions.

The purpose of the rest of this paper is to reflect on the successes and the failures of the reform of the NHS over the last four years, and to discuss the possible direction of the reforms over the next few years.

Key challengers for the UK health service

Obviously, any half-serious evaluation of the success or failure of the reformed NHS can only be made in relation to the achievement, or lack thereof, of objectives or changes on which there would be a broad consensus amongst professionals and politicians. Ideally, the wider public should be part of this consensus; however, this is difficult to achieve in practice, given the absence of mechanisms for doing so and given the highly personal view of individual members of society of health care priorities, coloured as it inevitably is by their personal circumstances and experiences.

For the purpose of this section of my paper, I have outlined a personal shortlist of key challenges/objectives on which there would be a managerial consensus in the service. In relation to each of these objectives, I offer an equally personal perspective on the degree to which progress is being made.

Objective 1

To establish a process through which the health needs of local communities are thoroughly and objectively assessed with a view to developing a professional, political and public consensus on local expenditure priorities.

In some respects, the above objective encapsulates the fundamental role of purchasers in the reformed National Health Service. (Their role to contract for the provision of services is covered later.)

From an admittedly narrow perspective as a Chief Executive of an Acute Hospital, I have not seen much evidence of purchasers paying more than lip service to this particular aspect of their responsibilities. Doubtless this statement does a gross injustice to many purchasing authorities up and down the country but there is a sense in which this objective is impossible in current circumstances. The difficulties, clearly not confined to the UK, are as follows:

- The political dimension to health care has made it very difficult for sitting governments to acknowledge the existence of informal rationing processes and the need to develop an open rationing process. (There are, however, recent encouraging signs in the UK that all the main political parties are beginning to accept the legitimacy of a cost/benefit equation in health care.)

- The public in the UK is conditioned to believing that each and every one of them has an absolute right to whatever health care they need at any given time in their lives. This even stretches to a widely held belief that it is the responsibility of the health service to provide (at the expense of the taxpayer) institutional nursing home care in the latter stages of their life. When ordinary members of the public are confronted with the knowledge that there is an expectation that the assets of a person in need of long-term residential or nursing home care can be 'claimed' to fund that care, they are both incredulous and deeply hurt.

  The idea of free health care 'from the cradle to the grave' is deeply embedded in the psyche of the UK population. Against this background, most purchasers who have made a genuine effort to engage their local community in any serious discussion of re-allocation of resources from one priority (or service configuration) to another have inevitably met with overwhelming resistance and a refusal to contemplate anything other than improvements on the status quo.

- Whereas purchasers are entitled to considerable sympathy when it comes to a question of prioritising expenditure programmes, it would be fair to ask how many have actually done a complete and objective assessment of the health status of their population, the medium- to long-term need for health care, and the extent to which the promotion of healthy life styles may change investment priorities over time.

  After five years of existence, possibly some purchasers are still driven more by general philosophies than they are by researched facts in relation to the current and future health needs of their local communities.

Given an unpromising resource position over the next few years and public demand to have unrestricted access to health care, it may be a legitimate strategy for purchasers to deal with priorities on an annual basis depending on which 'wheel is squeaking' at the time of annual contract negotiations.

Objective 2

Accelerated implementation of a 20-year-old policy to shift both emphasis and resources in health care from major hospitals to primary care and community services.

By definition, primary and community care services are so geographically and functionally disparate that it is difficult to generalise about the impact of the reforms on these services.

There can be no doubt, however, that the combined effect of creating purchasers with a remit to deliver this kind of change (and who carry no personal responsibility for managing the operational downside of moving resources from one part of the health system to the other) has been a real stimulus for progress in the development of improved primary care and community services.

This process has been greatly assisted by the introduction of more senior and dynamic management of community providers (whether independently or as part of an integrated hospital and community Trust) and through the professional, managerial, financial, and political opportunities that the reforms have afforded to general practitioner fund-holders.

Whilst there has clearly been some progress in the improvement of primary and community services nation-wide, characterised by pockets of significant progress, it would be wrong to suggest that gains made in this area can be said to be significant on a national scale or that there has been a radical shift of resources from secondary to primary and community care.

There are many reasons for this absence of a major breakthrough in delivering the primary/community care agenda, including the following:

❏ Purchasers have not been given the freedom by the government to scale down the volume of activity purchased in the hospital sector. This reflects the as yet unassailable priority in the public mind of acute hospital care above all other health care needs. It may be farcical, but it is true that the efficiency of the UK National Health Service is measured officially not by its success in keeping people well and at home, but by the size of the annual increase in the need to hospitalise the population.

❏ Notwithstanding the above point, there are genuine questions still to answer about the economic justification for re-distributing secondary care services to community-based facilities in a population which is substantially urbanised and for which most have no further to travel than a few miles to their nearest hospital.

❏ It seems that for some purchasers, moving secondary care services out of hospitals into a community setting has become a substitute for moving resources out of acute care into more traditional community services. For example, should purchasers be moving the vasectomy contract from the hospital to the local clinic, or moving out of vasectomies altogether and investing the money in improved domiciliary services to the elderly and their carers?

❏ The continued separation of statutory responsibility for personal health services and personal social services between health purchasers and local municipal authorities continues to blight the development of a fully integrated strategy for the provision of community and primary care services at the local level.

Objective 3

Improving the efficiency and quality of services.

This simply-stated objective would encapsulate a wide range of sub-objectives, including the following:

● the introduction of greater choice for patients, GPs, and purchasers;
● a focus on the needs of customers (patients) rather than health care professionals;
● the pursuit of effectiveness and efficiency in clinical services;
● the development of a quality improvement culture at the clinical level through clinical outcome measures;
● maximising value for money;
● improved internal and external communications.

It is in these areas that the reforms of the UK National Health Service have had their most immediate and fundamental impact. Whereas prior to 1991, health care providers in the UK could literally take their business for granted, the advent of contracting and competition has sent a shock wave through the NHS; this has had a particularly salutary effect on professionals working at the provider level and has been to the great benefit of patients.

Obviously, the impact of the NHS reforms at hospital level (and through the introduction of general practitioner fund-holders) has fuelled a political and public controversy over the reforms which has hardly abated over the last five years. An alliance of opposition politicians and provider-based professional associations has sought throughout this period to persuade the general public of the imminent collapse of the health service, despite the fact that the response to the threat of competition has seen what amounts to a cultural revolution in managerial and professional staff attitudes. Hospitals in particular recognise patients, general practitioners, and purchasers as customers, and for the powerful influence they have on the short-, medium-, and long-term prospects of health care providers and the people who work for them.

Despite the unabated controversy, hospital and community providers and the professionals who work with them have come to accept and adapt to the massive shift in power between purchasers and providers with the advent of the NHS reforms. As will be discussed later, this power has not always been wielded to the extent that it might have been or will have to be in the future, but the mere existence of it has had a galvanising effect in most provider units.

Cynics and opponents of the reforms argue that this improvement in attitude would have occurred under the old hierarchical regime. This is manifestly not the case and tends to reflect the views of individuals who have no extensive experience of the culture in NHS hospitals and community units prior to the reforms. The point is well illustrated by the issue of out-patient waiting times.

Prior to the reforms, the problem of excessive waiting times for specialist consultations had not been effectively tackled in most places. Whilst many consultants and managers were genuinely concerned to do something about these excessive waiting times, some consultants undoubtedly regarded long out-patient waiting lists as a status symbol (signifying popularity), whilst a minority may even have cultivated long NHS lists to encourage transfers to the private sector.

Whatever the reason, the plain fact is that no amount of exhortation, bullying, threatening, advice, studies, reports, etc. under the old hierarchical regime had any lasting impact on this problem. In these pre-reform days, sanctions for non-performance were almost inevitably visited on managers (if at all) and section clinical staff, however well motivated, were not given sufficient incentives to work with managers in providing lasting and significant improvements.

In those days, the balance of power between consultants and general practitioners was very much in favour of the consultants, who in the main made minimal, if any, efforts to establish levels of GP satisfaction with the services provided by the hospital.

In just four years, this situation has changed dramatically and only because some general practitioners have had the vision to recognise that ultimate power in the system comes through the control of resources and have opted to become fund-holders. The recognition by hospital consultants that local GPs now have the financial means to underpin or undermine local hospital services has forced them to confront the customer–supplier nature of their relationship with general practitioners.

At hospital level, the purchasing power of general practitioner fund-holders and the potential loss of millions of pounds worth of income has forced provider managers to take on their own professional staff over quality issues in a way that was unknown and unthinkable prior to the reforms.

There is hardly a hospital in the country that has not been working furiously to reduce out-patient waiting times across the board since the advent of the GP fund-holder.

The uncertainties which arise from competition and contracting have converted strategic planning, business planning, and objective-setting processes in provider units from superficial 'wish lists' to a serious plan for institutional survival that is now understood and contributed to by all the key professional groups.

Whilst it would be foolish to claim that in all the five areas referred to at the head of this section there has been substantial progress, it is fair to claim that there is substantial effort and some progress on all fronts.

Objective 4

Using the contracting process to implement changes in provider configurations.

An earlier section of this paper covered the objective relating to the shift of resources from secondary to primary care and this particular objective is focused therefore on the success of the reforms in producing a more logical and effective distribution of hospital services.

In many respects, the forces which are driving change in the distribution of hospital services represent the most urgent challenge to purchasers. This is because a number of the major influences on the pattern of hospital care in the UK have emerged independently of the purchasing process and will, over the next few years, force purchasers to confront contracting objectives which will bring them directly into conflict with the public and politicians.

Notwithstanding local purchaser and provider views about the desirability of geographically convenient access to hospital services, it is inevitable that a number of factors will ensure a continuing and steady reduction in the number of locations from which acute hospital care is provided:

❑ A continued and accelerated trend to organ-specific or disease-specific specialists based at bigger centres serving substantially bigger populations than presently served by most District General Hospitals, for example specialist cancer units.

❑ Changes in the arrangements for training junior doctors in the UK will shift much of the burden of day-to-day medical supervision of patients on to consultants and other career-grade staff. It is highly improbable that, given this change, it will be possible to sustain the number of hospitals currently capable of accepting 24-hour emergencies.

❑ The possibility that improved technologies and training of consultants will allow for partial decentralisation of specialist services currently provided at regional centres.

In spite of the intensity of political and public support for the retention of every service in every hospital, the impact of the changing pattern of hospital medical services will inevitably bring about at least a modification, if not the closure, of many services in many hospitals.

Purchasers may not have the luxury of limitless amounts of time to attune local populations to the impact of such changes if general practitioners begin to respond to the professional and legal pressure on them to make referrals to specialists rather than generalists. This will be particularly so as evidence builds which shows improved outcomes at major centres and specialist units.

Whilst it cannot yet be said that all purchasers have taken on the implications of these particular changes, the fact is that they will have no option but to do so. Moreover, it is difficult to imagine how the pre-reform organisation of District Health Authorities serving populations of 250,000 and managing their own District General Hospitals could deliver specialty rationalisations involving many specialties where the population base moves up to 500,000 people, with a change to a single main provider instead of the two or three currently providing the service.

At least we now have commissioning authorities responsible for contracting for populations of up to 500,000 people, which are in a position to use the contracting process to ensure an orderly transition to new hospital configurations unfettered, unlike their predecessors, by direct managerial and organisational links with the professionals affected by the changes.

Whilst it is obviously easier (on paper) for purchasers to impose fundamental changes in service patterns on providers through the contracting process, it remains to be seen if they can fulfil with similar 'ease' the unique and fundamental responsibility that they have for selling the changes to the local communities.

The public/staff perspective on reform

I suppose it is true that the majority of the public and the majority of people who work in the NHS would, if asked the question directly, proffer the view that the reform of the National Health Service has been a change for the worse as they see it. If pressed as to why they hold this opinion, most members of the public would eventually concede that their judgement is based on what they have read or been told and not necessarily on any adverse experience they have had of the NHS since the reforms were introduced. To a large extent, the attitude of the general public has been influenced by the ferocity of the national political debate on the National Health Service and in particular by the sustained campaign of opposition from organisations that speak nationally on behalf of nurses, doctors and other professional staff in the service.

If professional staff at grass roots level are pressed as to why they feel the NHS reforms have been bad for the service, many offer the view that financial considerations have replaced a commitment to the patients as the main driving force for NHS institutions. Further questioning often reveals that staff equate the drive for improved internal efficiency with an intention to diminish rather than enhance the level and quality of service to patients. Therein lies the biggest failure of the NHS reforms. Those who have sought to represent the reforms as a slide into crass commercialism have won hands down in the campaign to win the hearts and minds of the public and of the workforce. The advocates of competition in the purchaser/provider process, plus a concern for the needs of patients ahead of the needs of professionals, have failed to win the argument even in the face of considerable evidence that health care facilities are managed better, are run better, and are manifestly more responsive to their customers than was the case prior to the introduction of the reforms.

At the root of much public and staff concern about the NHS reforms, is a confusion between a deep and ultimately irreversible belief in an NHS freely available to every citizen at the time of their need, and a more questionable view that this guarantee can only be provided by institutions and staff which are safely and permanently located within the National Health Service itself.

The founding principle of the NHS, which enshrines the right of the public to free health care at the time of need, has been cynically represented by opponents of reform as being indivisible from their fight to preserve the organisational and professional status quo.

Problems with the internal market

Another major problem with the reforms has been the very nature of the internal market. Whilst all the key players recognise that a pseudo-market situation exists, the cutting edge of the competitive and contracting process is inevitably blunted by the knowledge that all the key stakeholders operate within an integrated National Health Service. Whilst this arrangement had the obvious advantage of proclaiming the maintenance of the NHS as an integral whole, it does have significant disadvantages as follows:

❑ It fosters the belief amongst providers that, when the chips are down, the political imperative in the NHS will be to ensure that they are looked after.

❑ Many professional and political networks straddle the purchaser/provider divide and exercise considerable, albeit unofficial and unaccountable, influence.

❑ There is a sense in which the contracting and competitive process is a more up-to-date version of the old hierarchy. Both purchasers and providers operate safe in the knowledge that there is a hierarchy to pick up the pieces if they make a mess of things.

❑ Allied to the third point above, there is a tendency for provider and purchaser chief executives to function as rivals and to pursue personal success to foster career aims within the wider National Health Service.

❑ The NHS is managed from the centre through the purchasing process, which means that the ultimate accountability of providers to central NHS management creates an imbalance of power in favour of purchasers.

The future

In the real world, the UK faces a general election by mid-1997 at the latest, in the run-up to which will be yet another fierce debate about the future of the National Health Service.

Obviously the high political profile of the NHS coupled with public anxiety about preserving the founding principle of this service will ensure that opposition politicians will promise to reverse or modify current reforms and the party in office will studiously avoid contentious new proposals.

The reality is, therefore, that in any circumstances some version of the purchaser/provider processes will be retained; politicians of all colours will promise to fulfil all public aspirations and many of the changes in the service that have to happen over the next few years will happen by default in an environment of continuing controversy and acrimony where changes are perceived as negative by local communities.

A future based on fudge and compromise (whilst a legitimate reflection of political reality) does not unfortunately provide very much in the way of a stimulus for animated professional debate over future options. On the assumption, therefore, that others in the UK will describe a future direction for the NHS which attempts to reflect political realities, this paper will now go on to take the role of 'devil's advocate' by exploring the case for a yet more radical phase of reform of the National Health Service.

Public purchasing/private provision?

Let us imagine for argument's sake that it were possible to persuade the British public that, in order to keep faith with the founding principles of the NHS from their point of view, what is required is that they should continue to have access to free treatment of the highest quality at the time of their need and in a convenient location. In persuading the general public of this core vision of the National Health Service, we might begin to separate in their minds their own interests as consumers of high quality, free health care from the interest NHS hospital and community providers have in convincing the public that they have an inalienable right to a collective monopoly in the provision of these services.

To complete what is admittedly something of a fantasy, given the political climate, let us imagine that we had indeed persuaded the general public that the survival of the National Health Service was not the same thing as the survival of the present network of National Health Service hospitals. What then would be the longer-term advantage of 'free' NHS health care delivered through a substantially more mixed economy of providers?

Major benefits may include the following:

1. Making purchasers more accountable and more visible

The responsibility of purchasers at authority, GP fund-holder, and locality level for securing the best services possible for their own community of taxpayers would be absolute and unambiguous if they alone were the standard bearers for the National Health Service. This would be a significant and fundamental benefit in comparison with the position now where the public has almost no understanding or conception of the role of purchasers in commissioning high-quality health care on their behalf.

The fact is that, at the present time, the wider public continues to link their own aspirations for the preservation and improvement of the National Health Service with the narrow and often self-interested aspirations of the health care professionals in the local hospital unit.

2. Unshackling the purchasers

The formal bonds which continue to link purchasers and providers within an integrated NHS have shown themselves to act more as a brake than a catalyst for change. This would only be a good thing if radical change were not both necessary and inevitable, which in the case of health care it most certainly is.

There remains an urgent and overwhelming need to tackle all the challenges, to which earlier sections of this paper have referred, in a substantially more robust way than hitherto. The widening gap between demands, needs, and resources calls for radical action and this is particularly so in relation to the overall organisation and the efficiency of providers.

Neither the old nor the new version of the NHS has shown sufficient willingness to tackle these issues vigorously enough; often this is due to the influence of political and professional networks which continue to operate on a NHS-wide basis both nationally and locally and serve to protect the interests of those employed in the NHS, rather than those to whom it provides services.

The creation of a thriving and genuinely independent provider sector in the provision of NHS services would do much to break the strangle-hold of the old institutions.

3. Changing public perceptions

Neither government nor purchasers can ultimately escape the need to introduce radical changes in the pattern of health care provision. However much the public and health care professionals demand the retention of the status quo, the hospital service in particular will need to cope with continuing service rationalisation with inevitable and major reductions in the number of hospital sites offering a full range of acute services.

In these circumstances, there is no particular advantage to governments in preserving the love affair between the general public and the local NHS hospital. There may be advantage in cutting this umbilical cord in the hope that the public will come to see changes in the pattern and location of hospital services in the same relatively detached way in which they have embraced the benefits to them of hypermarkets and supermarkets at the expense of local grocers.

NHS stalwarts would, of course, deride the comparison between health care and buying the family groceries as comparing provision of a basic need with ... another basic need. What is in no doubt is that the public has come to accept that the Sainsbury and Marks & Spencers of the retail world offer a mix of quality and value for money that it is worth their while travelling to get. If the public is willing to travel some distance, for example to the city centre or out of town, on a weekly basis for household commodities, is it inconceivable to imagine public acceptance of the benefits of travelling modest distances to get the best health care, given the need for hospital care is a rare event in the life of the average citizen?

4. Reaping the efficiency harvest

Most informed commentators within and outside of the NHS are well aware of the enormous efficiency dividend which would arise from the more rapid rationalisation of acute hospital services. In a true market situation, an equally substantial efficiency dividend would also emerge from the effect of a real competitive discipline on the currently huge variation in clinical practice and costs in NHS provider units. Such variations would be impossible to sustain in a system where objective comparison of competitive costs could be made against a tightly drawn service specification incorporating a measurable outcome requirement.

5. Making a reality of contracting

In circumstances where contracting and competition were for real, both purchasers and providers would have to adopt a much more mature and professional approach to the process than is currently the case. As has been alluded to in earlier sections of this paper, there is an air of unreality about the purchaser/provider process within the current NHS which arises from the existence of an organisational safety net which protects both purchasers and providers from any consequences of sloppy or incompetent contracting on either side.

In a situation where NHS purchasers were responsible for the transfer of billions of pounds of taxpayers' money to private health providers in contracts to provide local health services, there would have to be an enormous improvement in the quality of the purchasing process. Just to take one example, it would an almost unimaginable challenge for purchasers to understand the health care business in sufficient detail to allow them to produce a specification tight enough to satisfy probity standards for major contracts with the private sector. NHS purchasers could not get away with the embarrassingly crude approach to contracting which is currently the norm and which, in its ultimate manifestation, is characterised by a block contract that requires providers to meet every conceivable demand for a single fixed sum of money.

If a real market would create substantial pressure to improve the quality of purchasing, this is as nothing compared with the jeopardy in which providers would be placed if their response to this new circumstance were inadequate both in terms of service costs and quality and the quality of their own contracting processes. With no NHS safety net to cushion private sector providers from failed tenders, the professional complacency and resistance to change, which can be found in all provider units, would have to disappear overnight.

Providers who could not rely on tried and tested informal NHS processes to protect a weak position would quickly seek salvation by collaborative arrangements with neighbouring providers and would become overnight advocates rather than opponents of service rationalisation and in this way deliver the purchasers' agenda for them.

Conclusions

❑ The 1991 reform of the UK National Service has provided an organisational and financial framework for the NHS, which has more potential to deliver lasting benefits to patients than any previous regime.

❑ The internal market created in 1991 has had a profound impact on the attitude of NHS professionals working at provider level in so far as they have recognised the need to respond to and adapt to a shift of power to service providers.

❑ For reasons largely outside their control, purchasers within the reformed NHS have not been able to take full advantage of the potential to effect radical and necessary changes through the contracting process.

❑ The apparently unshakeable commitment of the UK electorate to the founding model of the National Health Service means that the power of the reformed NHS to deliver beneficial change will continue to be subject to political restraint.

❑ Notwithstanding the reality of the fourth point above, there is at least an academic case to be made for accelerating the reform process to a point where purchasers employed by the National Health Service commission and contract for free NHS care in a provider market that is substantially or wholly in the private sector.

Canada's National Forum on health and public–private care financing

Marie E Fortier

Editor's comment

Marie Fortier explores the issue of private vs public funding in light of the recently established Canadian National Forum on Health. Amid the financial constraints currently being experienced by the health care system in Canada, issues of health care delivery become obscured by preoccupation with funding sources.

In the past, Fortier explains, Canadian health care was tightly controlled through a system based on single-payor public funding. However, over the last two decades, this system has changed and for a variety of reasons, privately-funded services are becoming increasingly present. She explores the impact of this in the Canadian context, and warns of an emerging health care market for private insurance companies.

Fortier fears that the private sector's participation in the health care system can have a negative impact on some of the fundamental values underpinning the Canadian system. Privately run health care will create a two-tier system, something with which suppliers and people who are in good health have no problem, but which will actually be more expensive than a single-tier system. There will also be a real possibility that certain individuals or groups will be excluded from coverage.

Fortier calls for strong controls on the role of the private sector in health care delivery and offers criteria which can be used to measure the acceptance and appropriateness of health care delivery.

For inclusion in this book, the first section of this paper profiling the National Forum on Health has been summarised in order to focus more directly on the issue of private vs public funding in health care.

The CNFH and obscurities within the debate

The Canadian National Forum on Health is a three- to four-year process the purpose of which is to create public support for sustainable amendments necessary to maintain the national health care system. With diminishing federal assistance in health plans, and growing private expenditures, it was determined that a review of the national health care system was in order.

Forum members include regional and demographic representatives with expertise in the field of health care. The forum will attempt to involve stakeholders and the public in a variety of interactive ways including workshops, study circles, the Internet, etc. Various themes have been identified and specific groups within the forum, chosen to address them. These themes include: the determinants of health and their practical interventions; striking a balance in allocation of resources and action vs policy development; evidence-based decision-making and examining the barriers and incentives to change; and the implicit values which affect policy development and decision making.

While the debate on public/private financing in Canada can probably be described as perpetual, it has taken on special intensity since the beginning of 1995. Among other factors was the announcement by the federal Minister of Health that the government would act to ensure compliance with the Canada Health Act in those provinces which allow private clinics to operate with mixed public and private financing. The response from private clinic operators or those who saw future opportunity for private enterprise in health has been quite clearly in support of two-tier medicine. The announcement made in a February budget of future reductions in federal transfers of health targeted dollars only increased the interest in private health care on the part of its current and potential providers.

The discussion on public and private financing of health care in Canada is obscured by confusion between financing and delivery. Throughout the history of health care in this country, services have been delivered by 'private' providers. To this day, physicians are by and large considered 'private practitioners' unless they are employees of a health organisation and many private entities are involved as contractors or suppliers of goods and services. There may well be scope for private providers to compete for a larger role in the delivery of services which has been traditionally provided by the public system: could not hospitals award contracts to companies based on competitive bids for ambulatory services and day surgery? There are probably initiatives of this type under way now across the country. Important as this may be in terms of the management and efficiency of health services, it is not the policy question before Canadians in the debate over public/private financing.

The other subject causing confusion in this debate is the definition of a health service, or more to the point, the definition of what does not constitute a health service. For example, an obstetrical ultrasound prescribed for clear medical reasons is without doubt a health service. Does an ultrasound prescribed without clear medical necessity (a topic discussed later in this paper) constitute a health service? If not, should it be paid for privately? Should it even be performed in a health facility thereby being partly subsidised by public funds? If it is not allowed to occur at all in public facilities (assuming there is a way to stop the medicalisation of these procedures), should it be allowed to occur in completely private facilities – new-wave 'photography studios'? How should these 'studios' be regulated? Are there downstream effects of this on the health system? This area requires further examination and debate.

Who pays? Realities of the Canadian system

The Canadian health care system is characterised as a single-payor, publicly-financed system. While most public health funding comes from general tax revenues, both federal and provincial, some provinces have chosen other modes of additional taxation. Two provinces levy individual or family premiums and four levy payroll taxes.

Public financing has enabled fairly tight control over spending in Canada compared with the US with its multiple-payor, mixed administration system. However, the proportion of health expenditure financed by the public sector has decreased over the last two decades, from 76.4 per cent in 1975 to 71.9 per cent in 1993. Private-health expenditure has increased from 23.6 per cent of total health expenditure in 1975 to an estimated 26.1 per cent in 1993 (*see Figure 1*).[1] Public expenditure, in fact, has had a very small rate of growth in the 1990s compared with private expenditure. By 1993, growth in the public sector was down to 2 per cent over 1992 while the private sector was growing by over 6 per cent as it had been doing since 1990. Several factors have contributed to this. Canadian provincial governments have been implementing reforms in the 1990s and reducing health budgets at the same time. These reforms have included reduction of hospital capacity, capping of physicians' income, and de-insurance. De-insurance has taken several forms: services may be removed from the list of insured services (wart removal, physiotherapy, in-vitro fertilisation), individuals may become ineligible for certain benefits (drug plan change from universal coverage to more selective coverage), or the capacity of the public system is changed in such a way as to force the shifting of services from an insured environment (hospitals) to a non-insured or partially-insured environment (community and home).

Who are the private payors? The major payors of private health expenditures in Canada are employers, through private health insurance companies. Employers provide group benefit plans for their employees and their families as well as for retired employees. This benefit constitutes a portion of the compensation package but it also contributes to the cost of doing business. As the public sector manages to control its costs, the private sector loses control over part of its own. That clearly impacts on the economic outlook of the private sector, its relative competitiveness in the North American economy and its ability to contribute to economic growth in Canada. But there is more to that issue.

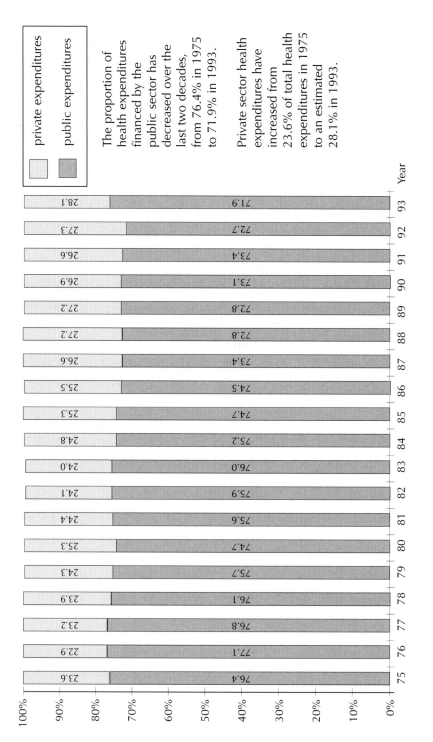

Figure 1 Percentage distribution of health expenditures by Sector of Finance
Source: Health Canada

Firstly, there are two different paradigms at play in managing costs and benefits in the public and private sectors. The public sector provides a public service. The private sector, on the other hand, manages benefits on an insurance model: risks are assessed, limits are established, co-payments or deductibles are levied and some benefits are not provided at all. The phenomenon of excluding individuals from coverage has not materialised yet in Canada, but it cannot be considered unthinkable, as employers and their insurers face tough choices in the future. One particularly vulnerable group of beneficiaries is pensioners. They have little, if any, power to negotiate, and are heavy consumers of benefits. If the private sector decided unilaterally to cut off these benefits, it is likely there would be enormous political pressures on governments to assume costs that have always been in the private domain or to reinstate benefits and coverage which have been reduced or eliminated.

A two-tier system

A significant challenge for Canada at this point in the public-private debate is the argument of under-funding or the even more surreptitious argument that allowing development of the private sector would lower pressure on the public system and enable governments to cut costs even further. Proponents of these arguments claim that insured services should and could be limited as long as those who can afford to pay are allowed to obtain privately organised and supplied services. The best-known Canadian example is free-standing eye surgery clinics where patients can have state-of-the-art operations with a minimum waiting time, in comfortable surroundings in which the patient is the client and the client comes first, at a cost of approximately $1,000. In the same community, free eye surgery is available at the hospital with a six-month waiting time, and in a typical hospital setting. This is clearly a two-tier system of health service and is contrary to the principles of the Canada Health Act (CHA) which tie compliance with federal transfers to provincial and territorial governments. The crux of the argument however is not CHA compliance but the fallacy that a two-tier system represents an advantage for Canadians. In reality, such a two-tier system would quickly expand to other areas, become increasingly attractive for private sector entrepreneurs (physicians, equipment manufacturers and private insurers) and inevitably cost more overall than a single-tier system. There are also issues of public subsidy to the private system, and physician cross-over.

Already, the idea of health care as an emerging market for private insurance is spreading. In the Winter 1995 issue of *IMPACT*, a newsletter published by the Canadian Life and Health Insurance Association, the President and CEO of a Canadian insurance company writes:

> *Health care is another area of great opportunity. Right now, private health insurance arrangements account for annual outlays of $7 billion in the context of Canada's*

total health care outlays, around $70 to $75 billion. Our industry share of the private insurance total is between 60 and 70 per cent – $5 billion a year. Our role will continue to be to complement and to supplement government funding. However, as governments withdraw from public programmes, more avenues open up. There will be continued growth in the need for private health coverage in tandem with government retrenchment in various plans and programmes.[2]

If that is not convincing, an article in the *Medical Post* of March 1995 describes how an American insurance carrier is offering Canadians a policy which provides for service in a US facility for policy holders whose names are on a Canadian waiting list longer than a prescribed time. The company's spokesperson is quoted as saying, 'In the next year or two, the Canadian system is going to open up to private care'. He does go on to say that what people have in Canada is equality but not freedom (of choice, one presumes). And that the two are mutually exclusive.

But this is clearly not the way Canadians see the issue. While some Canadians may believe the arguments in favour of increased private sector development, the vast majority continue to support a universal, publicly-administered system. There is ample polling evidence to support this. As the federal Minister of Health recently stated, the fit and fortunate tend to be supporters of two-tier health care. And they tend to be joined by the providers and suppliers who see a business opportunity.

Recognition that the role of the private sector in health must be controlled is growing. In the last year, all provincial Ministries of Health except one have considered this matter as it pertains to private clinics and have opted for a provincial solution. Regulatory control of this sector by provincial governments is currently being established.

The private payors are also increasingly concerned and looking for solutions. In an informal presentation to the Secretariat of the National Forum on Health last December, the Ontario Employer Committee identified a number of issues at the core of increased expenditures: the entitlement mentality among employees, the lack of incentives for informed consumerism, the lack of incentives for employers to sponsor health promotion programmes, and the productivity challenge associated with a healthy employee at work. The group stated that as stakeholders, their members do not have a voice in policy development. As managers of health insurance programmes, they have reached remarkably similar conclusions to those of the public sector: we need better practice guidelines for procedures, drugs, etc.; we need better information about cost-benefit ratios, and therefore more research; we need to share information more efficiently and effectively about best practices (or worst practices) and about individual patients and their history. They also anticipate the challenges that will be posed as the population ages, and are interested in alternative delivery mechanisms which may incorporate different incentive/ disincentive systems.

In the final analysis, we probably need to revisit the basis for determining insured services. When the Canadian public system was developed, most health services were provided either in doctors' offices or in hospitals. That has changed considerably. Furthermore, technology has issued the intervention possibilities in a way unthinkable in 1958 and 1966. And other health practitioners have emerged. Knowledge about efficacy and effectiveness of health services indicates that beyond the proven practices and interventions, some are unnecessary, some ineffective, and some doubtful. A new way of thinking about health services might be to create a set of criteria beginning with evidence of effectiveness, defining evidence to allow for quality of life considerations where appropriate. The second set of criteria might consider the appropriate setting(s) for the service and the third set could be appropriate provider(s). This would be the basis for policy, management and clinical decisions. This is the focus of the Forum working group on evidence-based decision making, which will complement the thinking on public-private financing and could provide the basis for modernised concepts of comprehensiveness while preserving universality, public administration, accessibility, and portability.

Conclusion

Convergence among public and private payors on the need to control overall spending creates a backdrop to this work. The National Forum on Health has developed a work plan that has every chance of getting at these matters both substantively and by focusing the public debate clearly on the core issues. The Forum has just begun its work and faces many challenges not the least of which are the expectations of governments, stakeholders, and the public. These expectations are not necessarily universally high, but neither are they necessarily consistent.

References

1. 'National Health Expenditures in Canada, 1975–1993', *Health Canada*, June 1994, p16.
2. Raymond Garneau, 'Looking into the Second Century', *IMPACT*, Canadian Life and Health Association Inc., Winter 1995, p10.

Managed care: pro or con?

In the United States a major trend has been a movement towards managed care. Much of this has been in the form of vertically integrated systems which provide all levels of care to the insured population. John King presents a paper which celebrates the successes of the Oregon managed-care system while Jim Mongan describes some of the untoward consequences of managed care.

Managed competition in Portland, Oregon

❧ *John G King* ❧

Editor's comment

John King presents a comprehensive picture of a successful managed competition system in Portland, Oregon. He asserts that there is value added when health care providers and health insurers share the financial risk in health care delivery. King suggests that combining these responsibilities encourages doctors to take a more active interest in how medicine is practised and to strategise on improving outcomes. These changes have also improved efficiencies in office expenditure and lowered overhead costs.

Managed-care plans tend to favour primary care physicians since patients find their care through them. Although consumer choice continues to dominate the system, the success of managed care has reduced hospital admission rates and shortened the average length of stay.

King identifies and discusses seven management challenges for systemic improvement to the Portland situation. They include:

- Changing organisational culture to a new way of managing and thinking.
- Creating new vertical relationships by combining services.
- Developing effective leadership especially among physicians.
- Improving horizontal management by developing better communications and better patient information transfer throughout the system.
- Bringing health professionals into management in order to make a more efficient and coherent system.
- Acquiring relevant skills in marketing, management, system thinking, etc.
- Improving quality and relevance of information in a more integrated system.

This paper has been edited and parts have been summarised to explain the case study of the Oregon health-management organisations, how they were introduced into Oregon and their impact on the five major players (insurers, physicians, hospitals, government, and employees).

Managed competition is one model of health care delivery that has gained acceptance in the United States. Several metropolitan areas in the US have a decade or more of experience in managed competition. They can serve as 'learning laboratories' for other communities or nations seeking to understand managed competition.

Portland, Oregon is one of the more advanced managed competition markets in the US. Managed competition has served well as a foundation for long-term, sustainable improvement in the health and delivery of health services to the people of Portland.[1] The greater Portland area encompasses four county jurisdictions and the total population is approximately 1.5 million people.

Oregon has a history of progressive ideas, liberal thinking and environmentally-conscious initiatives. For example, Oregon's state legislature enacted the country's first bottle-return law, which passed the state legislature in 1972. In the spirit of its progressive reputation, an historic precedent was set in the state's November 1994 general election. Oregon voters passed a physician-assisted suicide law, making it the nation's first state to legalise physician assistance of patient death by self-administration of prescribed medication. However, this law has been stayed in federal court due to protest by various citizen groups. Thus the law remains inactive.

The Oregon Health Plan is another example of this state's affinity for innovation. It was enacted by the state legislature in 1989. The idea emerged from state-wide forums in response to rising health care costs and an increasing number of uninsured and underinsured people. The health plan provides universal access to health care by using a combination of public and private insurance plans. This plan was crafted by health care providers, health care consumers, business, labour, insurers, and law-makers over three legislative sessions (1989–93) and embodies three major areas of reform:

❑ Expanded Medicaid to cover Oregonians below the federal poverty level ($991 a month for a family of three).

❑ A high-risk insurance pool for people unable to get coverage because of pre-existing medical conditions.

❑ Insurance plans and tax credits for small employers (three to 25 employees) who have previously not offered coverage to their employees.

Conditions fostering managed competition and the macro view of the US health care environment

Several strategies have been proposed to deal with the issue of rapid growth in national health care expenditure. Health care spending accounted for 14 per cent of gross domestic product (GDP) in 1992, compared with 5.9 per cent in 1965. As with access, there are several reform objectives centred around controlling costs, including limiting public programme spending by the federal government, limiting total public and private health care spending, providing greater incentives for cost constraints and eliminating factors that increase health care costs.

Health care reform in Oregon, especially in the Portland area, has moved ahead of the rest of the nation. This is largely in response to local conditions and market forces rather than government initiative.[2]

The presence of Kaiser Permanente in the Portland area is a factor that has greatly influenced the emergence and presence of managed care in this market. First introduced in Portland's shipyards in 1942 (and later in other blue-collar industries), Kaiser's health plan represented the first attempts to manage the health of a controlled, enrolled, employee population. Kaiser's Health Maintenance Organisation grew steadily as the first foray out of the traditional fee-for-service approach in a metropolitan market. Except for Kaiser's HMO plan, Portland remained largely indemnity, or fee-for-service, in most health insurance plans, until approximately ten years ago.

Up until May 1995, Kaiser was the market leader in terms of overall HMO enrolment with 25 per cent of the Portland market, but Blue Cross Blue Shield of Oregon's HMO plan, HMO Oregon, surpassed Kaiser's number at 26 per cent. Non-Kaiser HMOs have grown 92 per cent over the last five years, reaching 470,616 members in the non-Medicare market by the end of the calendar year 1994. The overall market penetration (the percentage of those under the age of 65 years enrolled in HMOs) was 43.9 per cent in mid-1994.

Kaiser is the market leader in the area's Medicare HMO market with 32,000 members or 34 per cent of total Medicare HMO enrolees. The overall Medicare HMO market penetration was 64 per cent in mid-1994. This represents one of the highest market penetration rates in the nation.

Also encouraging competition is the over-supply of hospital beds and specialty physicians, which has enabled plans to get price concessions and thereby gain competitive advantage and increase enrolment in managed-care plans.

The average bed occupancy rate is approximately 55 per cent for all hospitals in the greater metro area; 16 facilities provide twice as many beds as are needed. The number of medical specialists also runs higher than needed for this population base. Consequently, the over-supply and moderate demand have kept prices fairly stable and enabled insurers to obtain price concessions, thereby creating increased competition.[3]

Consistent, high-quality health care has encouraged HMO growth. Consumers who select HMOs can and do feel confident of quality. For example, the state's largest insurers, Blue Cross Blue Shield of Oregon, recently conducted a consumer satisfaction survey detailing perception and receipt of quality services as delivered by primary care physician providers. Five thousand randomly chosen patients of several doctors within primary physician groups were polled and 90 per cent said they would recommend their health plan to a friend; 88 per cent rated their satisfaction with the health care received in the four and five range (1 = poor, 5 = excellent). Surveyees defined quality as friendliness and courtesy of the physician, personal interest in the patient, thoroughness of examination, and attention paid to the patient's verbal comments.[4]

Primary care physicians in groups have promoted HMOs. PacifiCare, a California-based, group model HMO, entered the Portland market in the mid-1980s. The plan recruited the largest and best organised primary care groups in the area and offered both commercial and Medicare risk insurance products. The groups are prepaid, tightly managed, and have total risk for all physician services and shared (or partial) risk for hospital services. The Medicare risk product has been extremely successful, from a profitability standpoint, for both the physician groups and the plan. This success has funded the plan's growth as well as increased compensation for primary care doctors.

The participating groups have embraced the managed-care approach by encouraging patients to enrol in their health plans (and have been given incentives to do so). These grouped physicians responded to incentives offered through sharing risk on hospital services by becoming extremely aggressive in the management of hospital services utilisation. In effect, this action has set the standard for the community.

All players involved

The managed-care approach comprises all players: hospitals, physicians, payors and individuals. It also encompasses different financing options for employed persons, those on Medicaid, those on Medicare, and those utilising Worker's Compensation supplemental reimbursement.

Within the framework of managed competition, several sub-markets exist for the various segments of the population offering different insurance products. Large employers usually offer choices that include both managed-care and indemnity (or traditional fee-for-service) plans. Small employers can now provide health care coverage to their employees through the Oregon Health Plan's HMO plans and receive tax credits.

For the unemployed and those requiring government assistance, the government-funded Medicaid programme was expanded in Oregon to cover more individuals. The Oregon Plan strictly limits marketing to the eligible individuals. Enrolment and education is handled by a single organisation. Those over the age of 65, can get the government-funded Medicare, insurance Medicare and Medicaid which are both individual markets, where each person has to select a health plan. Medicare recipients can choose a Medicare HMO either through Social Security offices or directly through the health plans.

The trends in enrolment in managed-care insurance plans – Health Maintenance Organisations and Preferred Provider Organisations (PPO) – in the Portland metro area reveal managed-care's impact. According to recent data from the Oregon Association of Hospitals & Health Systems, Oregon is ranked first in the nation for total HMO market penetration; nearly 44 per cent of the four-county area population under 65 was enrolled in a health maintenance organisation as of January 1994. Portland also leads the nation in the percentage of its 65+ (or Medicare-eligible) population enrolled in HMOs at 64 per cent. The total state population enrolled in HMOs is approximately 30 per cent.

As of January 1994, the combined Portland, Oregon, Vancouver, Washington metro market led the nation in overall HMO penetration at above 60 per cent. The four other top markets (Rochester, New York; Madison, Wisconsin; Yuba City, California; and Stockton, California) averaged 59 per cent penetration.

This movement to HMOs and the resultant restructuring of Oregon's health care delivery system has significantly reduced unnecessary hospital utilisation and restrained health care costs. This data illustrates that using Oregon's hospital utilisation and cost experience as a model for the nation could accomplish much. Additionally, Oregon's experience shows that movement to a managed-care delivery and financing system, coupled with a market-forced focus on cost efficiency, has the potential to achieve significant savings in unnecessary hospital utilisation and overall health care expenditures.

Impact of managed care on key players in Portland

Insurers

The insurance product mix has changed dramatically: there is little traditional indemnity insurance left. The mix or market-place of current and emerging insurance 'products', has changed dramatically over the last ten years. Managed-care plans predominate and the traditional indemnity that is left is mostly with large self-insured employers and with union trusts.

Currently, Portland is experiencing a positive insurance cycle and profits are available. Health plans consciously favour Primary Care Physicians (PCP) in their reimbursement formulas, through the PCPs function as the health care gatekeeper. For example, HMO Oregon's Risk Sharing Plan involves target budgets for both PCPs and specialists. The PCPs have a significant financial stake in the performance of the specialists and hospital funds. In one recent year, HMO Oregon paid out about $12 million at settlement to providers, split evenly: $3 million to PCPs, $3 million to specialists and $3 million to hospitals. Although the PCPs are paid less for their services to HMO Oregon, their settlement values are equal to specialists or hospitals. Therefore, the PCPs are being rewarded for managing the target budgets to a surplus.

The tendency has been to shift risk to providers – physicians and hospitals – through capitation and modified capitation (shared risk) strategies. Portland-area providers have aggressively sought to share financial risk with health insurers. Two trends explain this development: competition for patients, and the historically low cost of care in the area. Health plans offering to share risk have been well received because providers have correctly viewed them as a way to maintain or increase the volume of patients. For example, a number of group practices encouraged PacifiCare to set up their first expansion HMO in Portland in the early 1980s. These medical groups have grown much larger, in terms of both physicians and enrolled members.

Primary care physicians see risk sharing as a way to control specialists, both in terms of patient care and financial reward. The second trend emphasises that risk sharing fits well when providers' practice style fits managed-care. Kaiser's influence over practice style, even among private practice physicians, has meant that the Portland area, historically, has low utilisation rates for hospitalisation, and lower-than-average physician compensation. Physicians realised that they could share financial risk with a health plan, and still succeed.

This shifting of risk has taken place both because health plans want to move risk to providers and because the more progressive provider/physician groups are asking for a greater sharing of risk. These forward-thinking groups can assume the risk and understand that with increased risk can come greater rewards.

As in the traditional insurance setting, the market remains highly dependent on brokers to market products to employers. Insurance brokers assume the role of the 'middle man' between the employer or the purchaser of a group health plan, and the insurance agent. Because the market rapidly changes and is increasing in complexity, employers rely on brokers to represent their company or group (also called population).

Besides the government-sponsored Medicare, seniors can opt to enrol in supplemental HMOs, each of which has adopted a different senior marketing strategy. Established plans have tried to capture 'ageing in' or near-retirement age persons who have had group coverage before they reached retirement age. Newer plans spend millions of dollars a year on direct mailings, mass advertising and promotions.

Physicians

Physicians are gathering together in larger and larger groups. The economic incentives supporting these decisions include streamlining office operations, reducing overhead expenses and gaining economic strength. Several types of arrangement have been forged and have succeeded. But usually primary care doctors join other primaries and specialists within single specialty groups.

There are a number of physician/hospital relationship arrangements and three distinct examples in the metropolitan Portland area. These three models include a pre-paid arrangement in which physicians exclusively serve enrolees (as in Kaiser Permanente), a system-owned practice ownership model (as in the Sisters of Providence), and a model of physician/hospital partnership (the model of Legacy Health System). Each modality contains its own set of economic incentives, doctor autonomy, success indicators, and risk share.

One element of common understanding among all three models is that doctors are now taking active interest in how medicine is practised and how outcomes can be positively maximised. The highest quality patient care depends on leadership exercised by both hospital administration and doctors. Hospitals and health systems encourage and assist physicians in transforming their practice patterns to maximise healthy outcomes.

By grouping and merging, physician-providers are building more efficient and comprehensive practices to manage care. These groups can manage their operations and patient care more efficiently through economies of scale, singular approaches to budgeting for reimbursements, group contract purchasing, shared overheads and increased networking opportunity.

Portland, with its Medical School and multiple teaching and research programmes, continues to be home for many graduating primary care and specialty doctors. Portland has the appropriate number of primary care physicians and an over-supply of specialists.

The appropriate ratio for primary care physicians vs specialists per 100,000 enrolees (or populations) is 32:68, according to Milliman & Robertson, Inc. The Portland metro area shows a 28:72 ratio (these figures do not include obstetricians/gynaecologists). The Portland area contains approximately 202 specialists for the top ten specialties. Milliman & Robertson puts the appropriate number at 90.[5]

Managed-care plans favour Primary Care Physicians. Health plans require patients to receive their care through PCPs. While individual health plans have slightly different definitions of PCPs, the disciplines included are: family/general practice, internal medicine, and paediatrics. Some plans also include obstetrics/gynaecologists.

The PCP will either provide or direct the patient's care. If the PCP can't take care of the patient him/herself, a referral to a panel specialist must be obtained. This health plan requirement severely limits the patient's ability to self-select any physician. The change in control of patient care results in overall cost savings and more status for PCPs. In this way, primary care income is increasing and specialists' income is being reduced.

The most extreme example of the shift in economic power are health plans that fully capitate PCPs. Specialists must negotiate contracts with PCPs, and are paid directly by PCPs. Hospital payment is also included in some contracts. PCP-driven medical groups have proved to be the toughest bargainers for specialty services in town. They have also pioneered new ways of paying sub-specialists, such as sub-capitation contracting.

Medicare reimbursement has also favoured primary care physicians through increased fees (via Resource-Based Relative Value Scale [RBRVS]). This relative value scale was developed by the government's Health Care Financing Administration for use by Medicare. The RBRVS scale assigns relative values to each medical service/procedure category code on the basis of the resources related to the procedure/service rather than simply on the basis of historical trends. The practical effect has been to lower reimbursement for procedural services (for example cardiac surgery) and to raise reimbursement for cognitive services (such as office visits).

Prepaying (or capitating) primary care physicians for all physician services (both primary and specialty care) establishes primary care as the purchaser of specialty service. Although this has not taken place on a grand scale in the Portland area market, to the extent to which it has happened, there has been significant change in the relative power of primary care and specialists.

Now, physicians are much more involved in managing the cost of care and monitoring utilisation of services, due to the shifting of risk. Providers demand greater involvement and control when they are at direct financial risk.

A recent nationwide study shows that physicians employed in managed-care settings can earn up to 38 per cent more than their colleagues in fee-for-service environments. HMOs and integrated delivery systems are offering more attractive and comprehensive incentives because they recognise that motivated physicians are great assets. Median annual pay for internal medicine physicians earning mostly managed-care revenues is $137,500, while their counterparts in fee-for-service arrangements earn $99,300. The study analysed compensation elements for 5,400 physicians in 46 medical specialties. Physicians with full-time administrative functions earned an average salary of $130,000; those with part-time administrative functions earned on average $160,000.[6]

Hospitals

According to quarterly data from the Oregon Association of Hospitals & Health Systems for the greater Portland area, in-patient data reveals a steady decrease in the length of stay, while actual admissions have remained relatively flat at levels equivalent to those in 1987. This drop in patients' length of stay is down from an average of 5.8 days in 1981 to 4.4 in the third quarter of 1994.

In-patient days is the total number of days among all patients in a given market. For the Portland area, in-patient days per 1,000 population in 1993 hit an all-time low of 410 per 1,000. For Portland, this represents a 15 per cent decline since 1991. The national average was 742 per 1,000 population for 1993.

This decline in census translates into an over-supply of hospital beds. Curiously, Legacy is the only system to decrease its number of hospital beds substantially. Legacy even closed one of its hospitals in 1992.

Besides the phenomenon of stable in-patient admissions, and declining lengths of stay and average census, there has been concomitant growth in out-patient surgery and out-patient visits. For Portland's 16 area hospitals, out-patient surgeries have increased 32 per cent in the last three years, with approximately 100,075 out-patient surgeries occurring in 1994 vs 74,100 out-patient surgeries that occurred in 1992.

To understand these market changes, it is also relevant to note that, similar to the phenomenon occurring with physicians who are forming economic units via larger and larger medical practice groups, hospitals are doing likewise by forming systems or networks, bringing multiple facilities under an aligned, centralised operational structure. This has happened with relative speed in Portland. Nine of the 16 metro hospitals are under the corporate structure of three systems. These systems form financially strong economic units that align with physicians and payors/insurance plans.

Physicians and hospitals experience continuing pressure to manage restructuring of care and its cost. Hospitals, through care re-engineering efforts, place emphasis on quality and case management to produce provable increases in efficiency and clinical quality. Other hospital system efforts include changes in non-direct patient care operations such as utilising computerised technology to track patients' charts, prescribed medications, and follow-up care as they move through the system.

Government

Government regulation has remained a relatively minor player in much of Oregon's reform of health care delivery and management.

After the Oregon Health Plan was enacted to provide basic care to all; the state government took advantage of existing managed-care plans, to manage care of Medicaid patients through capitated care reimbursement. Twenty HMO insurance plans throughout the state (13 in the greater Portland area) are part of the payor base for Oregon Health Plan enrolees. Enrolment, although higher than expected, stands at approximately 93,000 for the Portland area and has progressed steadily and smoothly.

Oregon's short-term experience has been very positive. Because care for the under-served is managed by PCPs, visits to hospital emergency rooms have declined. Legacy's two urban hospitals have experienced a respective 6 per cent and 21 per cent decrease of non-reimbursed, charity care given through the emergency departments.

Business/employers

Local employers and the business community have benefited by the stable, low price increase for HMOs. With the increasing prevalence in fixed-fee contracts, businesses have realised strengthened ability to plan for health care spending on employees. Multiple, high-quality insurance plans are available to small, medium, and large employers.

The public (through employers) has also responded positively to managed care, as evidenced by steady increases in HMO enrolment and demonstrated high levels of satisfaction. Abundant consumer choice still exists for the spectrum of health care insurance options.

Evaluating managed care in Portland as a foundation for long-term sustainable improvement in health and health system management

The Portland health system has been evaluated against four criteria:

1. Pursuit of value and efficiency with a sense of pride

Over the last four to five years, the competition between health plans in Portland has produced a positive environment for improving the capacity of the systems to increase efficiency and improve quality simultaneously. The competitiveness of the market place is growing and the robustness of the health plans and provider-delivery systems and their sense of pride and accomplishment is far greater than in regulatory environments of the 1960s and '70s.

Oregon health system spending is well below national averages. Per capita spending for physician and hospital services and pharmaceuticals is $1,500 per year. The national average is $1,800 per year. The competition in Portland has gained efficiency by substantially reducing the admission rate to hospitals and the average length of stay. Case management and clinical protocol implementation have reduced the use of unnecessary resources in the care of patients. Care-givers designed the approaches to care rather than having imposed external standards improving the acceptance of change.[7]

While these improvements are noteworthy, Portland has too many hospitals, hospital beds, and specialty physicians. The competitive market has reduced the use of services but has yet to reduce over-capacity of the system adequately.

Portland health systems have addressed clinical quality and service to patients. Continuous Quality Improvement (CQI) re-engineering, case management, and clinical protocols are common management processes used in the health systems to improve quality. Outcome studies have been launched more recently to determine the functional outcome of treatment over time. While it will be several years before outcome studies provide useful information at the same time, accreditation for all Portland HMOs is in the offing.

2. Influencing demand by informed public expectation

The large portion of the population enrolled in HMOs has been educated to expect to use a primary care physician, to have access to a restricted panel of specialist physicians, to be admitted to hospitals only when necessary, and to have physicians' extenders provide selected services in physicians' office settings. These and other practices of care management have enabled HMOs to influence the expectations and demand for service by enrolees.

Less well-developed is the penetration of basic preventative health measures among HMOs in Portland and in the US. Better patient education, systematic tracking, and follow-up of patients is required in order to improve the penetration of accepted prevention measures with enrolled populations.

In Portland, competitive health plans formed a collaborative organisation in 1993. Oregon Health System in Collaboration operates as a vehicle for competitive systems to conduct joint programmes in the community to improve health status. The first initiative sought to improve the rate of immunisations of children under five years of age. In 1994, more than 11,000 children were immunised in a state-wide effort. A programme to improve access to prenatal care is in the process of being launched.

Much is yet to be done in Portland, especially among high-risk population to influence the appropriate use of health care services. The Oregon Health Plan reform enrolled more than 93,000 Medicaid members in 13 existing HMOs in Portland in 1994. It is too soon to evaluate the impact on cost and use of services of this population.

3. Using the public/private mix

The Medicare and Medicaid programmes have operated, until recently, on fee-for-service and cost-reimbursement systems with too few incentives to manage demand for service or cost of service.

A capitated system of payment is working in Portland that is more of a public/private partnership. All Medicaid recipients are enrolled in existing HMOs and mainstreamed with other HMO enrolees. The plans are paid a capitated fee. Medicaid enrolees have choice among 20 plans throughout the state and choice of primary physician. Total Medicaid enrolment in the Portland area is 93,000.

It is too early to measure the long-term impact, but several short-term observations can be made:

- The cost per Medicaid member to the state is fixed in the short-term enabling the state to project costs more accurately.
- Customer satisfaction is above expectation.
- Physicians have had few problems with the patients in their practices.
- Health plans compete for the enrolment because the capitation rate is adequate.

In the Portland area, 60 per cent of the Medicare recipients have elected to enrol in optional HMOs. The enrolment rate is the highest in the nation for Medicare and continues to rise.[8] High penetration is due to the consistent high quality throughout Portland's health system, choice of multiple plans, low monthly premiums, and word-of-mouth marketing among seniors.

This public/private approach offers the best alternative to providing value, and political resolution to the spiralling cost of government-financed health care in the US. As yet, many parts of the country do not have a managed-care infrastructure sufficient to handle Medicare and Medicaid. The government needs to create better incentives to develop HMOs in other markets and capitate payment. Portland is proof it can work.

4. Maintaining public accountability

Public accountability in health care is extremely important for payors, providers, and patients. Only recently has information about cost and quality of care been made available to payors and the public in a form that is easily understood. Providers have tended to keep this information to themselves and have asked the public to trust internal systems to provide quality protection.

One of the benefits of the health reform debate in the US from 1990 to 1994 was improved public understanding that the cost and quality of health care in the US varies greatly from one community to another. The Health Care Financing Administration began releasing mortality information on hospitals. An accreditation programme for HMOs was established and a standard quality report card for HMOs was developed. As a result of these efforts, the data on health care quality is slowly being revealed to payors and users.

Health care competition is still driven almost exclusively by price and access to certain providers. Payors demand certain minimum quality and then price becomes the determining factor. In Portland, all provider networks are believed to be of high quality, and it is hard to differentiate quality among plans.[9]

Markets may change as better quality information is available and markets may become more responsive to quality particularly if price ranges narrow. It is also probable that as better quality information is available on competitive health plans, the variations of quality will diminish and levels of performance of all plans will improve, especially if the market is responsive to quality differences.

Maintaining public accountability will be assured if reliable data is available to the public about the performance of plans. This has not occurred until recently. Choice is also essential so individuals can choose from competing plans.

References

1. King, John G, 'Beyond Reform, What?' King's Fund International Seminar, Canada, 1995.
2. *Situational Analysis*. Corporate Development: Legacy Health System, July 1994.
3. *ibid*.
4. *Blue Cross Blue Shield of Oregon PPG Satisfaction Study*. Portland, Oregon: Bardsley & Neidhart Inc., November 1993.
5. *Managed Care Delivery System Analysis & Review*, Millman & Robertson, Inc., December 1991.
6. 'Report on Physician Trends'. *1994 Physicians Compensation Survey*, Ernst & Young LLP: Vol. 2, No. 10 (October 1994) pp3–4.
7. *Blue Cross Blue Shield of Oregon PPG Satisfaction Study*. Portland, Oregon: Bardsley & Neidhart Inc., November 1993.
8. *Capitation 1: The New American Medicine*. Washington DC: The Advisory Board Company, 1995.
9. *ibid*.

The failure of reform in the United States and its consequences

❦ James J Mongan ❦

➤ Editor's comment

In the United States, health care reform has been on the political agenda for more than 25 years, but it has been consistently deferred by the debates over how to finance it. While many programmes have been proposed, including employer contributions, individual contributions, and universal tax-based coverage, each one has failed for economic, social, or political reasons. The fear of tax increases instilled in the American people by politicians has exacerbated an already present perception of a decline of real income and a panic to survive. Many are apprehensive about the cost to them of supporting less fortunate people through health care reform.

Mongan identifies two problems which increase the pressures for health reform: the ever-rising cost of health care and the increasingly embarrassing number of uninsured. He challenges the notion that managed care will lead to lower costs and warns that often this term is actually a euphemism for managed enrolment. In many instances, healthier customers are selected to receive attention and Medicare expenditures provide an excessive amount to providers for their services, which increases health costs as well as managed-care profits.

He also predicts that more people will be uninsured. It will be harder to access care since uninsured people will not have the resources to enrol in managed health care plans. Those facilities that once were able to offer 'free' or 'charity' care, will no longer be able to do so if they are to remain competitive. The uninsured will be forced to go without care or will have to use already overburdened public facilities.

Mongan states that until a national discussion on American values takes place, health care reform will not occur.

Jim Mongan contributed a story from 1994 about Gerald Etter's thumb. We precede it with another one from 1969 that suggests that the fragmentation occurred far earlier (see pages 92–4).

This paper will be in two parts – a discussion of the failure of health reform in the United States in the past twelve months and a discussion of the consequences of that failure as we move forward in a mixed public/private system. The section on last year's failure will include a description of the process which led to failure and a description of the causes of failure. The section on consequences will focus first on the implications for the cost of care and then on the implications for coverage of the population.

Before going further, let me say just a word about my own perspective. I have worked on this issue for 25 years. I've had three opportunities to participate in this debate – first as a staffer for the Senate Finance Committee while the Nixon health insurance proposal was debated in 1974; then as the White House staff person when the Carter proposal was debated in 1980; and finally, as moderator and faculty co-ordinator for the Senate Finance Committee's weekend health care retreat in March 1994.

The key lesson I learned over this 25-year period is that the health reform debate, in Congress at least, is not now, and never has been primarily about health care – it is about the financing of health care. It is about who pays. This is where health reform died last year. The most important cause of the death of health reform was that avoiding tax increases and their thinly veiled cousin, employer mandates, took priority over expanding coverage.

Having seen this dynamic play out in 1974 and 1980, I laid out at the start of this round of debate in mid-1993, a chart (*see Figure 1*) which displayed how the deterioration of the drive for universal coverage would manifest itself. It describes in detail the elaborate congressional dance away from any hint of taxes or mandates.

President Clinton started – as had Presidents Nixon and Carter before him – with a proposal to achieve universal coverage financed primarily through an employer mandate. What the chart shows is the various compromises which would be put forth in an attempt to assemble a majority in favour of an employer mandate. First, limiting the benefits and thereby the cost of a mandate; then excluding small employers from the mandate; then extending the phase-in period for the mandate; and finally making the mandate conditional upon future circumstances.

Even with these compromises it was predictably impossible to assemble a majority and thus the employer mandate was abandoned. That led to a brief flirtation with a moderate Republican option, an individual mandate. But the individual mandate predictably failed because it required large subsidies which, in turn, required large tax increases.

So my assumption, well before the debate began, was that Congress would avoid all taxes and mandates and conclude the debate by setting an empty goal for universal coverage with no financing to reach that goal. Some said I was overly cynical, but in fact I had under-estimated the extent to which the debate would deteriorate. So in August '94, I had to prepare a second chart which illustrated how the debate could actually lead to diminished coverage.

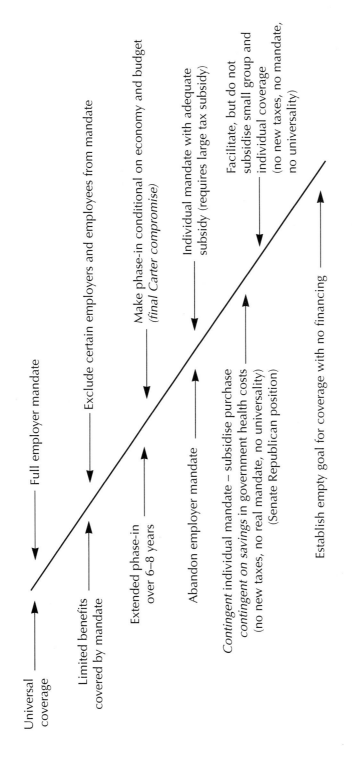

Figure 1 Slippery slope from universality – Part I

Prepared by: Dr James J Mongan, Executive Director, Truman Medical Center and Dean, University of Missouri Kansas City, School of Medicine

This chart (*see Figure 2*), which begins where the last left off, goes on to illustrate how Congress would abandon the goal of universal coverage; then overtly disavow the goal of universal coverage; then make clear that any expansion of coverage would be dependent on cuts in Medicare and Medicaid; and finally set deficit reduction through cuts in Medicare and Medicaid as a higher priority than any expansion of coverage. So at its conclusion, the debate had the potential to end up with no expansion of coverage and significant reductions in Medicare and Medicaid. I might add that is what was up for discussion in Congress in 1995.

Some may feel that this analysis is too focused on financing and may understate the complexity of the debate. I will concede that there undoubtedly would have been pitched legislative battles over other issues – how to pay doctors and hospitals, the role of health insurers, the structure of alliances – but these debates never happened in detail. The first and only battle last year, as in past years, was over financing – how to pay for it.

Now that I have described my view of the failure of health reform, let me turn to the underlying cause of that failure. Using the charts I have attempted to show the anatomy of failure. Now let me turn to the causes or the physiology of failure. To move back to an economic metaphor, what 'invisible hand' pushed the deterioration of the debate down the slope I have described? Well, the invisible hand is purely and simply the fundamental ambivalence of the American people regarding health reform.

Even though poll after poll consistently shows that the American people favour the concept of universal coverage by a strong majority, that majority evaporates quickly when you ask about their willingness to pay, through increased taxes or related employer and individual mandates which became viewed as the equivalent of taxes. So, as noted above, avoiding taxes and mandates took priority over expanding coverage and killed health reform.

What explains this unwillingness to pay for expanded coverage? Any answer must take into account the economic, social, and political context of the last two decades. Although economists may disagree as to the numbers, there is the strong perception, if not the reality, that real income has stagnated – that families are working harder to stay even. The social context is that people tend to take for granted the progress achieved through social insurance programmes like Medicare and Social Security; and they perceive little progress or achievement from welfare expenditures targeted to low income people. Politically, and this is very important, politicians from the court house to the White House have played to an anti-tax sentiment and have convinced Americans and American business that they are staggering under an oppressive burden of taxation that saps most productive effort. Although there is little evidence from other countries to support this belief, it is widely and deeply held.

This economic, social, and political climate fosters a self-centredness – a focus more on the individual's own needs than on those of the community. Some liberals

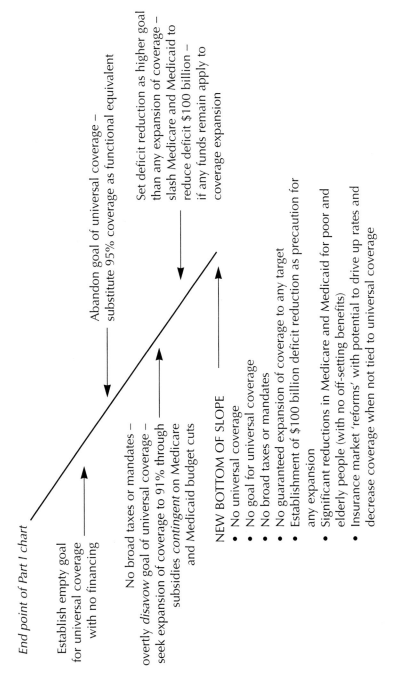

The slippery slope to diminished coverage

End point of Part I chart

Establish empty goal
for universal coverage
with no financing

No broad taxes or mandates –
overtly *disavow* goal of universal coverage –
seek expansion of coverage to 91% through
subsidies *contingent* on Medicare
and Medicaid budget cuts

Abandon goal of universal coverage –
substitute 95% coverage as functional equivalent

Set deficit reduction as higher goal
than any expansion of coverage –
slash Medicare and Medicaid to
reduce deficit $100 billion –
if any funds remain apply to
coverage expansion

NEW BOTTOM OF SLOPE
- No universal coverage
- No goal for universal coverage
- No broad taxes or mandates
- No guaranteed expansion of coverage to any target
- Establishment of $100 billion deficit reduction as precaution for
  any expansion
- Significant reductions in Medicare and Medicaid for poor and
  elderly people (with no off-setting benefits)
- Insurance market 'reforms' with potential to drive up rates and
  decrease coverage when not tied to universal coverage

Figure 2 Slippery slope from universality – Part II

Prepared by: Dr James J Mongan, Executive Director, Truman Medical Center and
Dean, University of Missouri Kansas City, School of Medicine

might use a harsher, more grating word – selfishness – to describe this state of mind. But many conservatives would use the phrase 'rugged individualism' to describe the same phenomenon, and defend it with pride. I am not a philosopher – I do not pretend to know at what point rugged individualism becomes self-centredness, or self-centredness becomes selfishness – or what the difference between those terms may really be. But I do believe that somewhere in here is where health reform died. And I further believe that until we, as a nation, make the right diagnosis, and begin an honest dialogue about our national values, about the balance between self-interest and community interest, we will not see our nation join almost all other wealthy nations in guaranteeing health coverage to all of our people.

Now let me turn to the consequences of the failure of health reform in the context of a public/private system moving towards managed competition and managed care. There were two engines driving health reform: the steadily increasing cost of health care, and the increasing number of uninsured. What will become of these two problems?

With respect to cost, there are a number of people who feel that this problem might be solved without federal legislation – by the market place working through managed competition and managed care. They see the United States rapidly evolving to a system where three or four health plans, paid on a pre-paid capitated basis, compete for enrolees in each locality, while fee-for-service medicine shrinks away. Frankly, I believe the jury is out on the question of cost savings. However, many in the United States are making the theoretical claim that managed care and managed competition will solve the problem of rapidly increasing health care costs. To bolster their case, they even point to some recent evidence that health insurance premium increases have declined for some large employers. This data, however, gives little hint as to causation. A number of things have been done by large employers in addition to stressing managed care. They have, for example, changed benefits and increased co-payments in many cases. There have also been underlying economic changes including lower concurrent inflation. A recent Milliman and Robertson study showed little relationship between HMO enrolment and health care costs, leading the authors to conclude: 'Evidence from our analysis indicates that managed care in the market place is currently having only a marginal impact on health costs.'

History would also give some cause for scepticism on this question. The San Francisco Bay Area has had managed care, in the form of the Kaiser Health Plan, competing with significant market share for 30 years with no evidence of health cost increases being any less in the Bay Area than elsewhere in the country.

There is even some reason to believe that, paradoxically, capitated managed care might drive costs up! A recent study by the US General Accounting Office has shown that managed care has added to the costs of Medicare. The reason for this is that, in many instances, managed-care plans are managing enrolment, not managing care. Managed enrolment, or enrolling only healthier members, can quickly drive costs up. Let me explain. Under Medicare, average expenditure per beneficiary is $4,020, but 90 per cent of beneficiaries have an average cost of approximately $1,340 and for the 10 per cent of Medicare beneficiaries with the highest outlays, the average expenditure was $28,120. If managed-care plans are paid the average cost to care for beneficiaries who incur costs substantially below this level, it drives up health care costs and managed-care profits! Until we are able to adjust premiums appropriately, this problem will haunt attempts to cut costs through managed care.

Two other points might be made regarding managed care. First, the label is in large part a euphemism. As indicated above, managed care has in many instances meant managed enrolment. In many instances it has also meant managed costs with plans negotiating lower fees from providers and negotiating generally crude utilisation controls. I would submit that few, if any, plans are managing care in the clinical sense. I assert this because I have asked the directors of many large managed-care plans how many of their enrolees have diabetes. Few can tell me. It is difficult to know how plans are managing care if they do not know which enrolees have what chronic condition.

A final point. The true test of how successful managed-care plans will be in controlling costs will come when we see their ability to limit new drugs, technologies and procedures in the face of continued consumer demand. As long as the *Reader's Digest* touts new medical miracles, there will be consumer and employee pressure for access to those miracles. Whether plans which noticeably restrict access to expensive services will continue to be offered by employers and chosen by employees, remains to be seen.

Now let me turn to the uninsured. This problem will definitely grow worse as a consequence of our failure to pass health reform while going forward with a private sector strategy of managed competition.

Two things seem relatively certain to happen in the future. First, the number of uninsured will continue to grow at a steady pace. The number has grown from 37 million to 41 million during the course of the recently ended debate over health reform. The underlying factors which have driven that number up remain in place. Even if health care cost increases moderate substantially, the cost of health insurance will remain beyond the reach of many small businesses and of low- and middle-income self-employed people. So it is reasonable to expect a steady increase in the number of uninsured.

Much more important, and of greater consequence, than the growth in the number of uninsured is the fact that these 40 million people will have a much more difficult time obtaining medical care in the future than they have had in the past. Why is this? Answering this question requires an understanding of how the health care needs of those without insurance are currently met. In general, one of three things happens today to uninsured people who face a chronic or acute health problem; in some cases, they go without care or defer care; in some cases they obtain care from tax-supported local public hospitals and federally funded health clinics; and in some cases they obtain care from private physicians and community hospitals. Over half the care to the uninsured is provided by community providers who write off the costs as bad debt or charity care and pass on those costs to paying, insured patients.

Here is the problem which comes about as a natural consequence of the nation's movement toward the much-touted 'market-based, managed-competition system' being widely adopted by the private sector. As we move, in most metropolitan areas throughout the United States, towards a system where insured people will enrol in one or another managed-care plan, serious problems will be posed for uninsured people who do not have the resources to enrol. Managed-care plans and their affiliated doctors and hospitals will not be able to compete if one of them is providing substantially greater amounts of 'free care' to the uninsured than other plans. The plan whose hospitals and doctors are providing more 'free care' will soon go under as the cost of this care drives its premiums ever higher. The only choice for competing plans who wish to survive will be to limit strictly any care to the uninsured.

This will leave the 41 million uninsured with no option other than going without care or falling back on the already under-funded and over-burdened public hospitals and neighbourhood health centres.

What happens to these people and what happens with health care costs will determine if we, as a nation, can walk away from reform. My own belief is that these problems will not disappear and that there are chapters of this story that remain to be written.

American health care system 1969: the story of Allen Roby

Six-year-old Allen Roby, youngest in a family of nine children, was born with a mild case of cerebral palsy which affected him only from the elbow down. He was classified as an epileptic and had occasional seizures.

April 1969: One day he had what seemed like a normal seizure and was taken to the hospital. This time he didn't come out of the coma. A week later it was recommended that the child receive a blood exchange. But this didn't help. The doctor did a craniotomy and a tracheotomy. A tumour was found.

July 1969: A few months later the child was taken to Rochester to have the tumour removed. During this time, Allen's brother and mother were admitted needing psychiatric care caused by their angst for Allen. Bills for such care were added to those already incurred.

cont.

cont.

October 1969: Allen was readmitted to the hospital for a few weeks until his family received a notice from the Utilisation Committee saying that he no longer needed hospital services and could not stay at the hospital. Even though the Roby family's insurance covered Allen's hospital stay for another two years, he was still told to leave the hospital. Because of the psychological state of his mother and brother, it was thought that Allen shouldn't go home.

November 1969: Despite this, Allen was taken home a month later because there were no other options. His parents took out a $5,000 loan to assist them in the costs: he had to have a bedroom downstairs, a suction, special diapers and gowns, all of which added to the already high medical bills. Allen stayed at home for three months.

February 1970: He was readmitted to the hospital for evaluation and was found to have pneumonia. He stayed at the hospital for 20 days and was then told again by the Utilisation Committee that he could no longer stay there, but that he needed custodial care.

April 1970: Allen was sent to a convalescent home where he stayed for over a month. Mrs. Roby received a call one day saying that he had to be removed. Assuming this was by orders of the doctor she went, in the rain, to get him. Allen had been at home for only two or three days before he started to develop a fever, and had pneumonia again. The family called the doctor who was surprised to hear that the boy had even left the convalescent home.

May 1970: Allen was readmitted to a convalescent home temporarily after appeals to the welfare office. Meanwhile his family looked for a foster home for Allen since he was too much of a financial burden for the Robys. They were spending $75–100 per week on medical bills and supplies for Allen, yet welfare would not help financially while the child was at home. Welfare said that if a foster home could be found and approved then he could go, but none that they found was accepted.

October 1970: The family received a call from the administrator of the convalescent home saying that Allen would be dismissed in a couple of days. The insurance company was only paying half the rate it paid while Allen had been in the hospital. The Roby family had the $5,000 loan to pay back, pending hospital bills and other medical expenses, not to mention their eight other children to maintain.

December 1970: On 23 December at 4am, the Roby family was called to come and pick up Allen and take him to the hospital. He died on 24 December.

paraphrased from *In Critical Condition:
The Crisis in America's Health Care,*
by Edward M Kennedy
Pocket Books, New York 1973

American health care sytem 1994: the story of Gerald Etter

When Gerald Etter severed his thumb with a power saw, he went to the nearest hospital for attention. North Kansas City Hospital was on the list of providers in his complete Cigna insurance plan and only a couple of miles from his house. So why did that hospital hand Etter his thumb in an ice-filled plastic cup and tell him to take it to St Luke's Northland Hospital? The following is an account of the events which transpired.

5 March, 7pm: Gerald Etter was cutting wood with a radial saw when he cut off his thumb between the nail and the top knuckle. His wife, Chris, drove him to North Kansas City Hospital within about ten minutes. There, his vital signs were checked and he was hooked to intravenous tubes and the staff applied a dressing. His wife was sent home to get the remainder of his thumb.

5 March, 8pm: After she returned to the emergency room, when the staff was about to X-ray her husband, Chris Etter was told that they may not be able to perform surgery to reattach his thumb. The hospital staff told her that Cigna Healthplan was difficult to deal with and therefore it would be better if the Etters were to go to another hospital. In the Cigna insurance package sent to the Etters, it was cited that emergency care would be provided anywhere at any time, and it listed North Kansas City Hospital as a provider even though unbeknowst to the family, it had been eliminated a few months before.

5 March, 9pm: On the way to the next hospital, Gerald Etter tried to remain calm. He had been given medication at North Kansas City Hospital which had numbed the pain, but his blood pressure was rising. North Kansas City had recorded it at 128/78; it was 150/90 at St Luke's Northland.

5 March, 9.30pm: When the Etters arrived at St Luke's Northland, a surgeon, Swanson, arranged for by North Kansas City Hospital, was waiting for them. Swanson told them that it was unlikely that they could reattach the thumb, not because of the time that had passed (now almost three hours since the accident) but because of the location of the cut. The tiny veins were too mangled.

As it turns out the hospital-hopping was for naught. Even though Etter had enrolled in the Cigna Healthplan in February, the insurance did not take effect until 1 April. So, at the time of the accident he was still covered by the insurance of his former employer. 'In all the confusion, none of this had to happen,' Etter said. 'Like my wife said, there's something wrong with this picture. I just can't put my thumb on it.'

paraphrased from 'Health System All Thumbs',
by Rick Montgomery
The Kansas City Star
3 March 1994

Who leads: hospitals or primary and community care?

The desire to focus more effort and more resources at the primary care level is widespread. But it is not always clear what this means. Once again we have two papers, both submitted from the UK, that present different perspectives on what community-based care means, and on how much of a good thing it is. Jenny Griffiths describes how to get appropriate community consultation on the planning of primary-care-led services, and Peter Wright declares his reservations about community-based care and about other aspects of the NHS reforms.

The battle for the future of health care
The development of primary-care-led purchasing in the English National Health Service

❧ Jenny Griffiths ❧

➤ Editor's comment

Jenny Griffiths examines the processes, structures and strategies involved in primary health care efforts in England. These efforts are based on general practitioner (GP) commissioning and a move away from the district general hospital model, into more differentiated service delivery: 'a shift from secondary care to primary care'.

Griffiths largely supports the expanded role of primary care. She advocates increased and more decentralised primary services and believes that this should be combined with the centralisation of secondary care.

She uses her experience in Hertfordshire as a case study to identify further the tensions surrounding the proposed changes. She believes that negative public reaction is connected to a perceived lack of accountability in the system ande a lack of evidence of the success of reforms. This makes it hard to communicate a reasonable strategy to the public.

She recognises that there have been difficulties in implementing the changes and argues that there has been a combination of the worst elements of different models of the NHS which include public service, business, GP focus and purchaser/ provider split. This mix has resulted in confusion and a lack of consensus regarding ultimate goals and strategies about the different levels of care. However, she believes that successful strategies are possible, perhaps through a combination of the best elements of the various models.

Parts of this article have been summarised to focus on strategies of how to achieve community-based health care, the difficulties involved in communicating information to public interest groups, and the public reaction to the proposed health care strategy in the Hertfordshire Health Agency case.

The purpose of this paper is to analyse some of the themes and tensions arising from the implementation of the National Health Service reforms, the creation of a primary-care-led structure for the NHS, the evolution of primary-care-led health care and the development of strategic purchasing. The latter will be illustrated through a case study of the Hertfordshire Health Agency's experience with the early stages of developing a health care strategy.

Health care nationally and internationally is moving away from the comprehensive District General Hospital model, which (with the general practitioner as its gatekeeper) has been the linchpin of the English NHS for the past 30 years. It is evolving into something far more complex and differentiated, with different types of hospital providing different services, and more care being delivered in primary care centres and in the home. The slogan used is the 'shift from secondary care to primary care'.

Primary care is seen as glamorous and innovative. We have come to believe that improvements in primary care can reduce the workload on hospitals, and that services delivered in other settings – in ambulatory and primary care – are somehow always better.

The time has come for purchasers to make this strategy more sophisticated. It is quite clear that services can be provided in a number of different ways outside hospitals, and examples abound: minor injury units, out-patient services in primary care settings, specialist nurses in the community for diabetes, asthma, stoma care, the occasional consultant community geriatrician or gynaecologist and so on. But we cannot yet provide much evidence for what is best in primary and ambulatory care, because of major gaps in knowledge of costs, comparative clinical effectiveness, and patient response. The evidence does not exist to support massive moves into primary care, even if the indications are positive and innovation is to be encouraged, especially if it is evaluated.

In many ways, ironically for a primary-care-led NHS, perhaps the most pressing strategic agenda is not the decentralisation of care for the less seriously ill, but the *centralisation of more specialised in-patient care*. This is because there is much clearer evidence that exists which shows a link between volume of care in particular areas and clinical outcomes than for the shift to primary care. Such linkages can be seen in areas as diverse as most surgery, coronary care, neonatal care and others – in other words, the common-sense proposition that practice makes perfect. In addition, changes in medical manpower from the reduction in junior doctors' hours and changes in junior medical training, which are gradually leading us to a consultant-provided service as opposed to a consultant-led one, should in themselves improve quality – but inevitably on fewer sites, since medical coverage will simply not be available.

If centralisation is a very important agenda, *ambulatory care* or *intermediate care* comes next. It is everybody's business: it should be delivered not only in general practice, but by Acute Hospital Trusts and Community Trusts. It is about cancer care centres supporting ambulatory oncologists on a hub-and-spoke model. It is about evidence-based purchasing for stroke services, applying the best knowledge to the organisation of care, so that people receive high-quality focused rehabilitation from integrated teams, probably based in small local hospitals. It is about nursing beds linking between the hospital and primary care. It may well be about highly specialised services such as ENT reaching out into local satellites to provide out-patient services, day-case surgery, and GP hotlines backed up with all the clinical expertise from the specialist centre.

Purchasing will also be more effective if it forgets about moving services from secondary to primary care as such, and instead focuses on strategies for client groups, particular needs or diseases, spanning all the settings for care – cancer services, stroke services, heart disease, mental health and so on. This population and patient-centred approach has to be the way forward.

Also very important indeed is the improvement of the essential primary care services, known in purchasing circles as 'core General Medical Services'. Too many general practices still do not offer the range of services that befits late twentieth-century primary health care: good health promotion, skilful counselling, expert diagnosis and apposite referral to other services where necessary, timely appointments, effective use of other primary care staff including practice nurses and nurse practitioners, chronic disease management, effective and appropriate prescribing of drugs, high-quality, out-of-hours services preferably not provided by deputising services, palliative and terminal care, efficient follow-up and information to patients. Ninety per cent of all health care contacts take place in the primary care setting.

Health care strategic priorities ought to be restated more clearly than the phrases 'secondary to primary care shift' or a 'primary-care-led NHS' might imply. A survey of the evidence and of priorities likely to achieve real health benefit for those suffering from common and serious conditions would suggest, as equal top priority: ensuring high-quality essential primary care services and more centralisation of specialised services on fewer sites; then ambulatory or intermediate care – acute care outside of hospital settings, probably on a hub-and-spoke model, i.e. backed-up by clinical expertise from the central hospital; and finally the development of extended primary care itself, including evaluation of service innovation. Strategy should also focus on the future structural organisation of health care, as centralisation of some services and the development of ambulatory care will mean that some hospitals have to change their role. Most importantly, it should focus on the needs of particular client groups with particular conditions, ensuring that their care is provided *in the most appropriate setting* – one of the slogans in Hertfordshire, and less divisive and artificial than the primary/secondary care distinction.

The main settings for care are: primary, ambulatory, in-patient and long-term care, together with health promotion. In an NHS where GPs are leading much of the service change it will, crucially, be the responsibility of the Health Authority to manage the implications of moving investment between settings, to minimise inequities in care and to prevent unnecessary instability and cost rises in both Acute and Community Trusts. Purchasers should accept such responsibility willingly, and not use our concerns about the management of change to hold back valuable GP initiative.

Developing a local strategy: the purchaser as enemy

So much for the theory. What is it like debating such a strategy with the public?

In a country that has not fought a major war for 50 years, everyday discourse – at least as conveyed by the mass media – still uses very militaristic language. Hertfordshire newspapers have amply demonstrated their view of their role as the 'people's champion', doing battle on the population's behalf with the Health Agency 'quangocrats': 'The fight for X hospital ... X hospital has not been saved yet ... stay of execution for X hospital ... hospitals under fire ...'.

It therefore seemed highly appropriate when the normally pacifist author of this paper found herself being given as a Christmas present by one of her staff, a copy of Sun-Tzu's *Art of War*, a classic text of military strategy some 2,000 years old, now read by Japanese and other businessmen who see life as corporate warfare. When the so-called 'public debate' on the Agency's strategy document was at its height, we found ourselves holding 'campaign meetings', 'tactical briefings' and, now that the battle is concluded (though the war is far from over), we talk of 'regrouping'.

The document instigating this battle was a genuine attempt at involving GPs, health care Trusts, opinion leaders and the general public, in the development of a health care strategy –*Towards a Healthier Hertfordshire – Where do we want to be?*. This discussion document had been preceded by two earlier papers. The second one, *Why Change?*, which rehearsed many of the reasons for change in health care encapsulated in Robert Maxwell's paper *Beyond Reform, What?*, had been accompanied by a programme of public meetings, but it had proved very difficult to generate public interest: apathy prevailed.

In the third document, published in October 1994, we asked for views on the choice between:

❑ Retaining the current pattern of acute and A&E (Accident and Emergency) services – which we stated would mean that an increasing demand for treatment would not be met and service quality would not improve as much as it should.

❑ Better specialised services in fewer locations coupled with more and better routine treatments more locally.

The document was based on the thinking outlined in the previous section of this paper. A review of A&E services was identified as a key step for change, because of the linkages between many relatively specialised acute services and the A&E department.

Where do we want to be? was received with outrage – in contrast to the apathy that greeted the earlier *Why Change?* document – for a number of reasons, the most important of which was that it was fundamentally opposed to the local population's view of their health care priorities. A reasoned view of this is contained in the following extracts from a local resident's letter:

> *Everyone I have spoken to … agreed with myself that option A [the current pattern of services] is by far the most preferable. We are all aware that more and more demands are being made on the NHS and most of us already realise that we will be expected to wait longer for treatment …*

However, it is a different matter to be told that we no longer have an A&E department close at hand. *People are more than prepared to travel to receive routine treatment, for which they have time to prepare and make travel arrangements* [my emphasis – the fact that 95 per cent of all health care would be available very locally was, to the Health Agency, a major plank of future thinking] … Accidents occur at the most inappropriate times, and under the most distressing circumstances. It is far more important for people possibly in immediate danger to be transferred to the hands of an expert A & E department in the shortest possible time. Given the choice, most people would opt for emergency treatment to be on the doorstep, ready to save a life when needed, and out-patient plus other routine treatment to be a car or bus-ride away.

Access (defined geographically only) was seen as far more important than effectiveness, equity appropriateness, value for money and so on. People defined the NHS as their local hospital. A 'cut' or 'closure' was seen simply as any change in location or geographical availability of a service, not as the amount of money spent on that service or the number of patients treated.

A second cluster of reasons explaining the adverse reception given to *Where do we want to be?*, related to difficulties in communication, perceived lack of accountability and political expediency. The Labour party sees any proposal as a cut, and takes every opportunity to exploit government policy to dismantle the NHS, as they see it. The Tories, on the other hand, typically do not support the working through of the NHS reforms at local level, and (have to) side with their constituents in undermining our work – they have to stand up alongside the publics view of the NHS to hold on to their electorate.

The media also played a crucial role: press and radio are the only means by which most of the one million residents of Hertfordshire receive any information at all on health debates (though we distributed 7,000 documents and spoke to 4,000 people in meetings). We are as far away as ever from informed public discussion of major issues of health policy in the media.

A third reason for the difficulties was that the separation of the NHS into purchasers and providers has brought into being a set of institutions, namely NHS Trusts, with a strong identity focused around a local general hospital. Whilst the commitment of these organisations to delivering high-quality health care is not in doubt, they also have a vested self-interest to defend their continued viability.

A final reason for the difficulty in gaining acceptance (or even a fair hearing) for the strategy was the hard fact that the failings of the District General Hospital were not known to the majority of the public. People assume that health care is of a uniformly high standard and always will be, regardless of how it is organised, so long as enough money is put into it. Inadequacies are attributed to lack of money rather than poor methods of organising and managing care.

It is also true that the evidence supporting change, as was suggested in section III, is not cast-iron: purchasing, like medicine, is about making the best judgement based on what information is available. The search for absolute clarity bedevils major issues such as support for the safety (at worst) or improved clinical outcomes (at best) of travelling further to A & E departments; or improved clinical outcomes and/or cost-effectiveness of more local provision of routine acute services.

So whose National Health Service is it anyway?

It is apparent from the above analysis that the NHS is subject to an unprecedented number of contradictory tensions at present in its quest to move towards a 'primary-care-led' service. If improving the health benefit offered by services is a primary aim of the NHS, it is not at all clear which of the key players actually owns that fundamental aim and, especially, the consequences of taking it seriously.

The general public remains generally satisfied with the care they receive, but are fearful of erosion of a public service and of cuts in local health care delivery. Most people have absolutely no idea of the reasons why services should change.

Central government policy is to use the NHS reforms as a lever to obtain better value for money, fundamentally from the existing pattern of health care delivery. Government policy encourages the expansion of primary care, but no published national policy document thinks through the consequences for hospitals of the re-provision of acute services in the primary care setting. Ministers take (sometimes very unpopular) decisions referred to them from the local level on a reactive, *ad hoc* basis but not against any national health care strategy, and these decisions are therefore almost always seen as negative by local populations.

Local politicians are, with honourable exceptions, generally driven by short-term expediency rather than the long-term view, which later can bring them no particular rewards.

GP fund-holders are highly effective at purchasing short-term improvements to health care. But they are pragmatic tacticians, not strategists. They focus on the particular, not the general, and their perception of what is required often varies dramatically between one practice and another.

NHS Trusts exist to manage the effective and appropriate delivery of the services that are required. The main secondary purpose is to ensure their financial success.

Which – if one holds to the view that the evidence supports considerable change to the way in which services are delivered – leaves us with purchasing authorities as the only 'champions' of large-scale change. Through something called 'public involvement', they are miraculously meant to square the circle and make the intolerable acceptable to local populations!

The NHS could be said to be caught between four different models of its identity and purpose. They can be described as the public service model, the business/consumerist model, the GP-led model, and the purchaser/population model. The current culture and systems contain elements from all four models, with resulting confusion both internally and externally. The main elements of each model are sketched in the following:

Public service model

- National command and control structure
- High internal motivation, goodwill, low rewards
- Utilitarian ethic
- Low public profile
- Very uninformed public
- Locally unaccountable
- Fairly well-controlled systems
- Hidden bureaucracy
- Encouraged by general management 1985
- Otherwise predates 1991 reforms but some elements of central control strengthened since

Business/consumerist model

- Internal market for provision of services
- Competition
- Choice for patients
- Passive patient – active consumer

- Fuels demand and expectation (e.g. Patient's Charter)
- However, public still largely hostile to 'business ethic' in NHS
- Greater efficiency/value for money
- Devolution from Centre
- Higher £ rewards for managers
- Unaccountable locally

GP-led model

- Transfer £ power to GPs
- Patient-responsive
- Makes service change happens
- Reaches hospital clinicians
- Apolitical – no political involvement/no external accountability
- Very limited public involvement
- High management costs
- Fragmentation

Purchaser/population model

- Rational
- Needs-led
- Effectiveness/evidence
- Paternalistic/patronising
- Priorities/rationing
- Long-term planning
- Values-driven
- Cumbersome/slow
- Public/political confrontation
- Seen as unaccountable

The NHS is struggling to come to terms with the ideological and practical divides between these four models. The ideal would be a mix of the strengths of all four: the high internal motivation of public service; the efficiency of the business model; the patient-responsive delivery of GP leadership; and the focus on effective services of good District Health Authorities. Achieving the right blend will take enormous effort over a long period of time.

In the meantime, we need a coping strategy both locally and nationally.

An acute provider clinician's perspective

Peter D Wright

Editor's comment

Peter Wright is more sceptical about the reforms than Jenny Griffiths. He too believes that they have been marked by confusion and conflict. He argues that while the intention was to improve patient care and decrease costs, there have been few such results. In fact, if the overall objective of these reforms was to maintain the underlying principles of the NHS while moving towards a market-driven system, it has not been met. There has been a failure of market forces accompanied by an erosion of the principles.

Although in his paper, Wright's comments are general, he has particular difficulty with the move to community-based care. He believes that there is no clear understanding or agreement about what would constitute community. Despite the many confusing views about the nature of community, there has been a headlong rush to extract resources from clinical care in hospitals. There seems to have been little thought about the consequences to clinical care. A good example is the concentration of acute care into fewer centres. This forces patients to travel further for care and contradicts the stated aim of providing care closer to those who need it.

Similarly the result of other changes is to substitute improved instrumental measures of care delivery for genuine clinical improvement. Reducing waiting times can eat up resources that might be better used to provide more and improved clinical care.

Introduction

This paper is intended to review the impact of the health care reforms in the National Health Service in the United Kingdom from the perspective of a clinician working in an acute hospital within a regional referral centre. The paper recalls the reforms as they were first proposed and then analyses their impact upon such a centre, attempting to place them within the perspective of the other quite radical and parallel changes that have occurred within the Service at the same time, and tries to assess whether or not there has been any added value arising from the reforms, and if so, for whom. One should perhaps reflect that the reforms did not occur in isolation, but were merely the latest in a series of changes looking at various aspects of resource management within the NHS, which date back to the original management budgeting initiatives in 1979.

The evolution of health care in the United Kingdom since the government white paper and subsequent legislation to reform the National Health Service provides many lessons on the pitfalls involved in radical change to services which most of the population have always taken for granted.

The government proposed seven key changes:

1. To make the health service more responsive to the needs of patients, with as much power and responsibility as possible to be delegated to local level.

2. To stimulate a better service to the patient, hospitals would be able to apply for a new self-governing status as NHS Hospital Trusts, (with powers of self-determination similar to those of a private sector business).

3. To enable hospitals which best meet the needs and wishes of patients to get the money to do so, the money required to treat patients would be able to cross administrative boundaries.

4. To reduce waiting times and improve the quality of service, to help give individual patients appointment times on which they can rely, and to help cut the long hours worked by some junior doctors, 100 new consultant posts would be created over the next three years.

5. To help the family doctor improve his service to patients, large GP practices would be able to apply for their own budgets to obtain a defined range of service direct from hospitals.

6. To improve the effectiveness of NHS management, regional, district, and family practitioner management bodies would be reduced in size and reformed on business lines, with executive and non-executive directors.

7. To ensure that all concerned with delivering services to the patient make the best use of the resources available to them, quality of service and value for money would be more rigorously audited.

However, the underlying principles of the NHS were to remain, but with a determination to obtain better value for money, with a move towards a market-oriented payor–provider relationship, together with a shift away from hospital-based acute care towards a more community-based service.

Lying behind these ideas there appears to have been a tacit assumption that such a change would give improved patient care at reduced cost, with consequent added value for the taxpayer, government, and patient. However, subsequent events tend to indicate that considerable uncertainty remains as to what, if any, value has been added and for whom.

The impact of 'Reform' in practice

The subsequent progress and associated problems may perhaps be illustrated by the changes that have taken place in the Northern Region of England around Newcastle upon Tyne.

This area formed what used to be known as the Northern Region which had its own strategic Health Authority, and consisted of 14 health care districts focused upon a population centre, which managed about 65 hospitals between them. Newcastle itself formed a focus with its medical school and its associated specialist centres, and provided general acute services to Newcastle and the immediately surrounding districts and more specialised services to those districts further away. The population served by the region was approximately three million.

Under the previous arrangements, large centres such as Newcastle were given extra resources in recognition of the significant proportion of work that came from surrounding and more distant districts which was partly specialist referral work, and partly general acute medicine or surgery which needed to go to Newcastle for a variety of other reasons. Under the newly introduced 'purchaser–provider' split, the individual Health Authorities were funded on a capitation basis to provide health care for their District population, taking into account such issues as cost, quality, quantity, equity, and accessibility. It was thus inevitable that there would be a radical restructuring of the service with the larger centres of population losing funding to the surrounding purchasing districts, with consequent effects upon the size and configuration of the hospitals and primary care services both in the centres and surrounding districts.

As the implications of these changes were digested, there was a growing nationally driven pressure to enhance the role of primary care, moving as much resource as possible towards supporting the patients within their homes, together with a strong locally driven will to see the development of local hospital services. In Newcastle, the potential consequences of these changes soon became clear, in that there would soon be a radical reduction in resources, and that an equally radical reappraisal of the shape and size of hospital services within Newcastle and the surrounding districts was necessary. For some time there had been three major hospitals in Newcastle: the Newcastle General Hospital which was over 100 years old, was situated in the more deprived area of the city, and had been based on the old workhouse and poor law hospitals; there was then the 'grand old Teaching Hospital', adjacent to the university, The Royal Victoria Infirmary, that saw itself as the centre of the medical academic universe and arbiter of all significant decisions; last, but not least, there was Freeman Hospital, a brand new 'upstart', given to the loyal city fathers by an appreciative socialist minister, with the idea that it might one day replace the old General Hospital. In addition to these, there was a variety of other small and large psychiatric and geriatric hospitals within the city. The consequence of the reforms was that there was a general acceptance that it was an appropriate time to review the provision of acute hospital services in and around Newcastle.

In April 1993, a meeting was convened in a neutral venue to produce the Acute Services Review. The meeting was a gathering of representatives from the main provider institutions within Newcastle, the university, primary care and the local and immediately contiguous health districts, together with facilitators who had particular knowledge of methodologies for estimating bed and specialty configurations, together with the wider financial implications of major changes in hospital estates. The co-ordination of the Review was monitored by the Regional Health Authority together with the local Newcastle Health Authority.

It was clear at an early stage in the discussions that there would be a significant reduction in acute beds within Newcastle with a shift of the more general services back to the home districts. There was a consensus that this was desirable; however there was difference of opinion as to the magnitude of any such shift. The number of acute beds in Newcastle at the time was about 2,500 for a city population of 285,000 within a conurbation of about one million. Projected bed numbers for Newcastle ranged from 1,300 by the most enthusiastic District purchaser to 2,200 from the much more cautious and conservative providers. In addition to these issues, the purchasers wished to see some of the resource tied up in capital such as buildings and equipment to be released to gradually enable them to develop services within the community.

After several days' discussion, evaluating several models of hospital and specialty configurations, it was decided that the best option to provide a comprehensive acute service for the needs of the citizens of Newcastle, at the same time as maintaining specialist services to the region, would be to concentrate all acute services on the two sites at the Royal Victoria Infirmary and Freeman Hospital, giving a total of 1,800 beds. It rapidly became clear that this solution was politically unacceptable to many of those representing primary care, many of whom worked close to the Newcastle General Hospital, who believed that that hospital must be preserved at all costs as a service to patients in the west of the city. A compromise was reached that would preserve the General Hospital as a 'new-style Community Hospital and Ambulatory Care Centre in which general practitioners and hospital doctors would work together'. Unfortunately no one participating in the Review was able to define exactly what was meant by the term 'Community Hospital'.

As a result of the Review a statement of intent was issued, but unfortunately no record of substance of the review was ever prepared or circulated to any of those involved or interested. On the basis of the discussions, steps were taken to establish a new NHS Trust based on the community services for the city combined with what would remain of the Newcastle General Hospital. A degree of consensus was achieved as the agreed solution did maintain the integrity of the acute and specialised services within Newcastle, and, if followed through, would allow the hospital estates in the city to be rationalised with the release of about £20 million (up to 20 per cent of expenditure) for redistribution by purchasers.

Following these discussions, a period of *public* consultation was entered into, both on the subject of the withdrawal of acute services from the Newcastle General Hospital and the formation of the new City Trust. During this process two things rapidly became clear: firstly that there was a very strong body of opinion that it should be the Royal Victoria Infirmary that should close with the preservation of the Newcastle General Hospital; and secondly, during the incubation period since the conclusion of the Acute Services Review, the concept of the new-style general hospital had changed, partly because the general practitioners had neither the time nor the wish to work in that environment, and partly because those involved in the planning of the new Trust had suggested that there should be an Ambulatory Care Centre where all out-patients and all day-case surgical procedures in the entire city would be undertaken. The consequences of this latter proposal caused considerable consternation, particularly because at least 50 per cent of the surgical workload undertaken at the other two acute hospitals was undertaken on a day-care basis. If all this work were to be transferred to the General Hospital site, the hospital was likely to be larger than that which existed before, thus undermining the whole point of the Review.

At this stage the entire debate upon both the deployment of acute services in Newcastle and the content and size of the City Trust on the Newcastle General Hospital site became more difficult because of the lack of an agreed reference point with regards to some details of the data considered and discussions which took place at the original Acute Services Review. Each of the interested parties was reiterating a view as to the outcome of the Review which reflected their own position within the debate, with the result that all involved were rapidly reaching widely divergent views about the meaning and recommendations of the Review.

The influence of changing staffing structures

The continuing progress of the Acute Services Review proposals in Newcastle has been modified by a number of external influences outside our control which mainly affect staffing of the hospitals, particularly junior doctors. There have been two national initiatives. The first was the expressed intention to reduce the working hours of junior doctors in hard-pressed posts. This was much needed because the pressures under which such people worked were intolerable and change was necessary. This process has progressed rapidly over the last two years and is actively managed from the centre by the Health Services Management Executive working directly with hospitals through regional offices. At the same time as this initiative was proceeding, a further initiative led by the Chief Medical Officer, Professor Kenneth Calman, was put in place to restructure the professional training programme for junior doctors. This has modified training in many desirable ways, which parallels training in Europe and should improve the consistency of training programmes.

One of the side effects of this programme is that an individual hospital may not have as many junior doctors to work in its units, and the junior doctors may be less experienced for a given grade than previously. If this effect is combined with the reduction in the hours a junior doctor can work, the obvious outcome is that there will be insufficient 'doctor hours' to do the work that was done previously, and there will be a consequent reduction in productivity. It is proposed that there be a radical increase in the number of consultants within the service to provide a more consultant-based service, with its implied improvement in quality of service for the patient, which is to be welcomed. However, although the management executive has provided modest resources to pump and prime a number of new consultant posts to enable the new junior doctors' hours to be achieved, purchasers seem unwilling at present to recognise that as an increased cost of service – which they will have to fund if a service is to continue.

A further manifestation of the complex pressures which providers are now having to pass on to purchasers, relates to the ability of a provider to deliver a 24-hour, seven-day service, within the constraints of junior staffing that now exist. The consequence of the more rigidly structured professional training programmes which now have to be provided, may make it difficult for an average district general hospital to provide an emergency service. For example, a trainee in surgery should be working as part of a team, with junior house officers below him and full senior support above, together with access to appropriate anaesthetic, intensive care, and investigational services. Already we are beginning to see that hospitals which are unable to provide 24-hour cover by junior house officers, have had higher professional trainee posts removed, prejudicing the ability of the hospital to deliver a safe emergency service. In situations such as those proposed for Newcastle, if all day-case procedures were taken to another hospital from which all other acute services had been removed, the training programmes would become unrecognised by the various Royal Colleges because of either the lack of day-case surgical experience in the main acute hospitals, or because of the lack of acute support services where the day-case surgery was done.

A further dimension which complicates our ability to resolve the problem is that there appears to be a reduction in recruitment: there is currently quite a severe 'skills' shortage at sub-consultant level in many specialties and it is getting increasingly difficult to fill consultant posts even if funds are available; in addition there is some evidence that there is a degree of reduction in recruitment into training programmes. There is particular concern that even with positive discrimination, the proportion of women in most post-graduate specialist training schemes falls well below the 50–70 per cent proportion found in most medical schools. In addition, it is becoming apparent that, in some areas, as many as 20 per cent of graduates in medicine have stopped practising within three years of qualification.

It is these staffing issues which are rapidly becoming a controlling variable in the ability of providers to deliver service in the United Kingdom, and it is being considered by many that the impact of these changes could make the consequences of the purchaser–provider split pale into insignificance. It is quite possible that in the near future many purchasers' prime consideration is going to be whether or not they can afford the resources to staff a 24-hour service and in which hospital; any contracts for patient care undertaken by that staff would be a bonus.

The evolving purchaser–provider relationship

Increasing problems are being encountered in the relationships between purchaser and providers. Those purchasers in the main centres, who have lost financially through the introduction of capitation-based funding, are encountering serious problems funding the needs of their inner city populations, often with a high deprivation index. At the same time many of the purchasers from surrounding districts who gained financially from the re-allocation of resources, spent the additional funds on projects that they saw as a higher priority. Unfortunately now, they are finding that the patients they thought they could manage within their home district, still require treatment in a major centre, and they no longer have the resources to support this. In addition, in response to the centrally driven move towards the dominance of primary care, significant amounts of resources have been taken out of the acute hospitals and used to develop many cherished projects within the primary care sector. Consequently, many purchasers are now encountering the problem that there are not enough acute beds remaining in the hospitals to contain the workload, particularly now that increasing problems are being met in delivering the community care services by the local authorities within the more restrictive financial regimes with which they are now having to contend.

The results of these changes are that the service is now encountering the reality that there is a pound (£) for patient care. If 'Mrs Smith' becomes ill and requires care, she can either have her pound spent on her behalf by her purchaser in an acute hospital provider or in the community. It can be appreciated that if it is possible, and the care can be provided with similar quality at home, then this would be preferable. However, it would seem that in many situations the care at home actually costs two pounds, or even more likely, the pound for 'Mrs Smith's' care has been spent on some other cherished project such as a counselling clinic for pregnant teenagers. Unfortunately 'Mrs Smith' is still ill and requires treatment and has been admitted to hospital as an emergency, exceeding the contract to which the purchaser has instructed the provider to manage, resulting in further unproductive conflict.

The impact of a 'patient's charter'

The current situation is compounded yet further by a strong move by the government to ensure a continuous stream of 'good news' about the National Health Service. This is perhaps best manifested by *The Patient's Charter* which sets standards for such things as waiting times for out-patient appointments and waiting times for admission to hospital. These are all excellent objectives; however there is a cost, which does not sit well with the limitations facing both purchasers and providers. Indeed if, for example, the waiting times for out-patient appointments and operations in orthopaedics alone are to be fulfilled there will have to be a dramatic increase in the number of surgeons, operating theatres and beds; this would leave few resources for any other aspect of acute care, and even less for community-based services. The situation is now reaching such absurd proportions that purchasers are threatening financial sanctions against trust hospitals who do not work within the waiting time constraints. Meanwhile, the same purchasers have not placed contracts with the trusts of sufficient size to enable all the patients to be seen and treated within the time limits. Little effort is being made to prevent primary care doctors referring patients for treatment, and even less to prevent patients seeing their doctor in the first place.

Perhaps the most serious consequence of this process is that the efforts of all those concerned in the delivery of contacts for care are being devoted to ensuring delivery within the constraints of contract numbers and *Patient's Charter* considerations. The priority for care on pure clinical considerations is now rapidly becoming secondary. We have seen over the last three years of the contracting process a 100 per cent increase in the number of patients who have had emergency surgical procedures. On looking back at the records of these patients, it is becoming clear that a significant proportion would have received a higher priority on clinical grounds, and would have been treated sooner, before becoming an emergency, if greater priority had not been given to other patients, often with non-urgent conditions, either because they were the patients of a GP fund-holder or were on a waiting list that was likely to exceed an arbitrary length.

Where is the added-value?

It is becoming increasingly clear that the reforms as they were originally introduced are not working as they had been intended. The concept of a purchaser–provider split implied the development of a 'market' which would have meant there being winners and losers. It has become obvious that few have had the courage to face the political consequences of losers. Unfortunately, it would seem that there are very few within the service who are satisfied with progress to date. Those in the medical profession seem highly dissatisfied. Many of those involved in primary care with a Health Authority as a purchaser are particularly dissatisfied because they see that many of the changes being introduced in the name of primary care are not those they see as a priority. They feel that they are less able to admit their acutely ill patients to hospital than before, most attempts at consultation by their purchasers being seen as cosmetic and ineffectual. The fund-holding GP is, in general, the most satisfied professional who has, by using the market, been able to improve the care he can give his patients. Within the hospital service, morale is extremely low, partly because of the reforms. There have been radical changes in career and staffing structures. In addition the involvement of clinicians in management has been very variable. Although there has been an increase in clinician support to managers, their real management authority has been limited by the circumstances in which managers find themselves, usually with relatively short fixed-term contracts related to performance. In this environment there is no way that a chief executive is going to allow a clinician with a secure contract to have real management authority with consequences that could affect his own job security. However, the increased exposure of the clinicians to purchasers has been an interesting and enlightening experience, particularly because it has emphasised the divide between the primary care professionals and the purchasers who are apparently buying service on their behalf. It is now a frequent experience to find complete accord between primary care and secondary care professionals about the quantity, case-mix, and quality of care required. The only dissenting voice being the purchasing health authority with resource constraints or direction from above.

We are now reaching a situation where we have a service in which the original freedoms for both providers and purchasers are being steadily reduced. Increasingly dominant central controls introduced from the management executive through their regional offices now affect details such as the deployment of junior doctors and other staff, and often quite minor capital development; a process which has been described as – 'management by faxed press release'. We even see groups of purchasers who during contract negotiations tell NHS Trusts that they will have a 'financial allocation' crudely assessed, irrespective of the anticipated workload. Perhaps the most disappointing feature is the complete lack of value-for-money purchasing, with resistance to case-type disaggregation and the significance of benchmark comparisons. Many of these changes make one seriously wonder whether there have been any reforms at all in the service. The bureaucracy that was in place before the reforms still seems to be there, now with different titles, but doing the same things as before. The most unhealthy aspect is the change in attitudes, where healthy and constructive criticism of what is happening is no longer acceptable; this has been regrettably exemplified by a recent series of articles in the *British Medical Journal* entitled 'Stalinism in the NHS'.

In terms of any value added by the 'reforms' to date, this is much less easy to determine. Particularly if it is recognised that one of the reasons for the change was the difficulty that would be encountered in funding the public expectations for comprehensive health care, particularly in a country where this has become regarded more as a right than a privilege. In these circumstances it may be naïve to conceive that there could be added value for anyone in these changes, where the tacit object was to re-organise a form of rationing of health care. We are in danger of ending up with a system where the gainers seem to be either those who have been, or are likely to be, on long waiting lists and those who would benefit from care within the primary care setting, at the expense of those who might benefit from care within an acute hospital. Having seen how the 'reforms' are actually working there are many who are increasingly of the view that the old system of rationing by clinical need and prioritised waiting list may not have been quite so bad after all. Where resources are limited it is inevitable that a judgement is going to have to be made by someone. In such a case, the best value may not be obtained by allocating resources on the basis of length of time on a waiting list rather than on clinical need or the ability to benefit from an intervention.

When considering where we go beyond the 'reforms' in the United Kingdom, it is extremely uncertain whether we have really undergone a reform, and whether that reform is really what we think it is. If a group of health care workers met together to discuss reform, they would undoubtedly agree it was necessary; but when each participant was questioned separately, it would become clear that the only reason that agreement had been reached was that each participant had a different perception of the meaning of the term 'reform.' It is only when introduction of reforms is attempted that these differences become apparent. Similarly with 'added value', in an arena where resource is finite, it is becoming clear that the cost of adding value for one player in a game, is likely to result in reduced value for another.

However, there have been some benefits. Contracting when allowed to flourish does give a transparency to what can, and cannot be delivered with given resources and investment in skills and facilities. Unfortunately, there is a degree of political edginess both nationally and among purchasers about taking uncomfortable choices, which are not necessarily shared by those in clinical practice.

An additional benefit of the changes is that they have challenged the traditional vested interests of the range of professional, historical, and trade union groups, and created considerable movement from the traditionally perceived roles of the various partners within health care.

In the final analysis, the most challenging hurdle yet to be crossed is to agree to a common currency which should probably be based around some aspect of clinical effectiveness, so that all involved in provision of health care may account more effectively for the use of finite resources. With the passage of time it has become clear that there is potential for significant 'added value' from the reforms, which include an appreciation of what can and cannot be delivered, a greater degree of openness in the process of decision-making, an acceptance of individual and corporate performance review, and more appropriate and patient-centred investment decisions. It is unfortunately becoming clear that there is a lack of commitment to the 'reforms' from many health care professionals, both purchasers and providers, such that we are in danger of seeing two health services emerge: the one that the purchasers and providers think they are running; and the service that is really running where the GP deals directly with the hospital specialist who treats the patient on clinical merit and to hell with the contract. Hopefully, sufficient courage will be displayed to allow the freedoms possible within the reforms, as originally proposed, to be exercised – enabling full advantage to be taken of the added value that should result for patients, purchasers and providers.

2 Divisions & splits after restructuring

Part 2 examines some issues still to be resolved post-restructuring:

- *the unmet needs of Aboriginal Australians*
- *the ethnography of health care tribes*
- *the limits of simple fixes*

On the first day of the conference, representatives of each country presented a 'national update' describing changes to their health care systems over the last few years. All countries have experienced major changes. The values keeping health care systems together have begun to unravel. There are growing policy differences in Canada and Australia between central and state or provincial governments. There are major problems about adequate coverage in South Africa and the United States. The consequences of the introduction of commercial incentives and other market forces are critical in the UK and New Zealand.

Michael Decter's review of Canadian health care describes the national values that provided a coherent basis for the different territorial and provincial health care systems, values which are subject to increasing financial pressures. Now health care in Canada is in as turbulent a state as systems in other countries. Canadians are 'smug no more'. A new pessimism has emerged along with conflicts about fundamental Canadian values related to health and social support. The differences get worse as time goes on.

Talk about split values was followed the next day by discussions about fragmentation and the financial constraints which have led to restructuring everywhere. Financial controls are becoming stronger. But fragmentation continues: in most countries deep divisions in health care remain. The major splits addressed in discussion were:

- Between the various providers inside institutions.
- Between institutions and the larger system.
- Between health care providers and the public.

Many of the papers describe these three splits. And in many of them the divisions remain after restructuring. Ken Jarrold thinks that special effort must be made by managers to heal the splits with clinicians. He also identifies the adversarial relation between purchasers and providers. Don Schurman sees that regionalisation will not by itself solve the problem of the relationship between the large tertiary care centres and the rest of the system. Nor will it improve the connection between providers and the public. Frank Burns believes that commercialising health care will help to heal the split between providers and the public, while Marie Fortier is concerned about a growing split in values between institutional providers and the larger system. John King believes that managed care will bring all the providers together, while Jim Mongan fears that the split between providers and the deprived population will grow. Jenny Griffiths is also concerned about the split between providers and public and believes that it can be eased by more and better public consultation. Peter Wright feels the division between institutions and the larger system is critical.

The split between providers and public concerns Robert Maxwell enough to be one of the focuses of a presentation to the Management Committee of the King's Fund. In it he states:

> [I] ... was struck by conclusions coming back from this year's King's Fund International Seminar ... The seminar focused on the question – in the six countries represented – 'Beyond Reform, What?'. In other words, what should those responsible for leading and managing health services be thinking about, beyond reorganising them? One diagnostic conclusion was that in most countries what the managers and the politicians are doing differs greatly from what actually matters most, which is the delivery of clinical services day in, day out, and actions that shape health. Nor, typically, is there a close link made by managers between what they want and the fears of the public at large. So reconnection and a renewed sense of what the NHS stands for are needed, which of course includes efficiency, but is primarily about effective and compassionate care.

A further and more drastic division shed new light on these splits. The third day of the conference was devoted to discussions about health care services for native people in North America, Australia, and New Zealand. Health status and health care are only two of the many areas where the Aboriginal population is disadvantaged.

Unmet health needs of Aboriginal Australians

Peter J Brennan & Michael Gracey

Editor's comment

Peter Brennan and Michael Gracey put the current situation of the Aboriginal people in Australia in context through a brief history. The dramatic effects of the colonisers led to fundamental changes in the Aboriginal people's way of life, and left them at a serious disadvantage to non-Aboriginals. Health care statistics demonstrate that in every aspect, Aboriginal people are more susceptible to disease and death. Although since the 1960s, there have been substantial changes, these have been restricted to the area of infant and child health, while maternal health standards, for example, are still far behind those of non-Aboriginals.

Several particular reasons are cited as to why Aboriginal health care is in such poor state: a failure to develop policies to link the provision of services with preventative strategies; severely poor environmental health conditions which lead to an increase in disease and also affect nutrition and lifestyles; a lack of Aboriginal involvement in the decisions, the development and the delivery of health care plans. The main underlying reason seems to be a long history of profound cultural difference which has included exploitation, misplaced attempts at assimilation, and serious misunderstandings over hundreds of years. It is in this broader context that health care efforts have failed.

As a result, the problems related to involving the Aboriginal population in health care planning cannot be resolved by simply delegating Aboriginal people to carry out non-Aboriginal policies. A re-evaluation of the content, priorities and concerns of Aboriginal health needs to be undertaken in the context of greater respect for the differences between Aboriginal values and those of the rest of the population.

There are some signs that things are changing. There is more Aboriginal involvement: partnerships are being formed among communities; and medical services are beginning to be controlled by the Aboriginal people themselves. But, according to Brennan, there is still a long way to go.

The Australian land mass was previously joined by a land-bridge to the large island of Papua New Guinea to the north and separated by a short sea voyage of 50–100 km from the outer islands of South East Asia. This bridge was submerged and Australia became an island at the end of the last Ice Age and its human inhabitants, the Aboriginal people, remained isolated from the rest of the world for 40,000–50,000 years; there is radio-carbon evidence of Aboriginal habitation in the Swan Valley near Perth back to 38,000 BC. During this very long period of isolation, the Aboriginal people adapted well to their environment and developed complex systems of language, lore, rituals, traditions and beliefs. They were pre-agriculturists and were the largest and most successful of the world's hunter-gatherer societies.

All of this changed irreversibly in the late eighteenth century when Australia was colonised by the British. Colonisation at Sydney Cove in 1788 was followed shortly afterwards by large outbreaks of infections in the Aboriginal population, including smallpox, typhoid fever, dysentery, influenza, and pneumonia. These disease outbreaks were devastating and were followed, over subsequent decades, by similar outbreaks in other parts of Australia as European settlement spread and the Aboriginal people became dispossessed and marginalised by the colonists. The destructiveness of infectious diseases in this immunologically naïve population extended to the effects of sexually transmissible diseases, like syphilis, and was compounded by the squalid living conditions that became the lot of the Aboriginal population, as well as by the damaging impact of alcohol on their traditional society. These and other negative impacts of non-Aboriginal occupation led to a widespread expectation that the Aboriginal race would 'die out'; this has not occurred but a situation has been reached where standards of health in the Aboriginal community are consistently worse than in the rest of the Australian population. Indeed, the Aboriginal people have been described as 'the unhealthiest sub-population in Australia'; in almost every disease category, their rates of hospitalisation and mortality exceed those of non-Aboriginals, often by factors of five times, ten times, twenty times, or even more.

Overall, the relative rates (RR) of hospitalisation of Aboriginal people (i.e. vs non-Aboriginal) in Western Australia for some selected diagnostic categories are:

- infectious and parasitic   5–6:1
- diabetes   4:1
- respiratory diseases   5:1
- injury and poisoning   4–5:1

Relative rates of hospitalisation for certain conditions tend to peak at particular ages as the following examples show:

- admissions for infectious and parasitic diseases peaking at 0–5 years   5:1
- diabetes admissions peaking at 40–50 years   12–20:1
- mental diseases admissions peaking at 35–40 years   8:1
- respiratory diseases admissions (at 50 years of age)   12:1

There have been some improvements in Aboriginal health over recent years, but the overall rate of change in Aboriginal health compared with that of non-Aboriginal people is disappointingly slow. In Western Australia, for example, it is projected that in the year 2000:

❑ The Aboriginal : non-Aboriginal standardised death ratio will be 2.8:1 for males (3.0:1 in 1989–91) and 3.6:1 for females (3.7:1 in 1989–91).

❑ The Aboriginal infant mortality rate will be 15.7/1000 live births (16.3/1000 in 1990) and 4.9/1000 for non-Aboriginal people (6.1/1000 in 1990); the rate ratio will, therefore, become worse.

❑ Life expectancy for Aboriginal males (60.6) will be more than 16 years shorter than for non-Aboriginal males (77.1 years).

❑ Life expectancy for Aboriginal females (63.4 years) will be 18 years shorter than for non-Aboriginal females (81.4 years).

The disproportionately high Aboriginal death-rates are cause for serious concern. For certain conditions the mortality rate ratios (compared with those for non-Aboriginal people) are much higher; for example:

- deaths from respiratory diseases   4:1
- deaths from digestive system diseases   5–6:1
- deaths from diabetes   6–12:1
- deaths from genito-urinary diseases   7–17:1
- deaths from injury and poisoning   4:1
- deaths from mental disorders   5–10:1
- deaths from circulatory diseases   2:1

These few examples show that health standards of Australia's Aboriginal people are, undoubtedly, far worse than those experienced by the rest of the Australian community. To begin to understand the causes of these blatant inequalities in health and their precursors, it must be appreciated that these people exemplify a Fourth World population. These are communities that are characterised by their experience of being colonised, or of being a minority in relation to the dominant, encompassing state. Many of these communities have been forced to assimilate, losing most of their land and their economic base, and therefore their autonomy. The fundamental changes that European settlement imposed on Aboriginal life led to a loss of control over their own destinies – they became outcasts in their own country and excluded from the resources, wealth and other advantages enjoyed by the rest of Australian society.

Aboriginal people experience significant and serious socio-economic disadvantage. This includes poor housing, overcrowding, inadequate hygiene, rudimentary education, unemployment, restricted access to medical services, and widespread nutritional disorders. These difficulties are complicated by the very limited involvement of Aboriginal people in decision-making in affairs (like health services) that affect their own health and well-being.

Aboriginal people had sought to publicise Aboriginal disadvantage and improve their participation through various organisations such as the Aborigines Progress Association from the early 1900s. However the depth of social awareness or concern for Aboriginal need was late to emerge and real progress did not occur until the mid-1990s.

The poor state of health of the Aboriginal population became recognised among non-Aboriginal Australians progressively from the mid- to late-1960s: first within the health professions, then, increasingly, by the Australian public and by politicians. Recognition of the unacceptable standards of Aboriginal health coincided with the Federal Referendum (1967) which, for the first time, saw Aboriginal people counted as Australian citizens, gave them the franchise, and granted them some other basic rights including equal pay for equal work and the right to drink alcohol. These fundamental changes in the circumstances of Aboriginal people were followed by an intense interest in 'the Aboriginal health problem' and many government-funded strategies and programmes intended to help improve Aboriginal health status. Despite the deep concern shown by many Aboriginal and non-Aboriginal people, this period of activity was characterised by considerable levels of Aboriginal and non-Aboriginal conflict over Aboriginal advancement policy, priorities and process. Aboriginal health advancement was not isolated from these turbulent times and was in many circumstances at the anterior of conflict. After a quarter-century of effort and controversy, it is timely to examine what changes have occurred in Aboriginal health.

Some of the initiatives have been very successful, these include:

- Substantially reduced infant mortality rates (from about 70/1000 in the late 1960s to about 15/1000 today; this is still more than double the non-Aboriginal rate).

- High coverage rates of protection of Aboriginal infants and children from vaccine-preventable diseases.

- Greatly reduced hospitalisation rates of young Aboriginal children for respiratory and gastrointestinal infections.

- A steep decline in deaths of Aboriginal infants and young children from gastroenteritis and dehydration.

- Control of leprosy in areas where Aboriginal people were previously affected.

It is quickly apparent that many of these improvements have been in the area of infant and child health and in response to classical public health interventions, such as immunisation and close maternal and child-health surveillance programmes. But even in the area of maternal and child health, improvements have been limited; maternal health standards fall well behind those of non-Aboriginal women and there is little evidence of improved nutrition and growth of Aboriginal children. A longitudinal study from the Kimberley region of Western Australia, for example, has shown no improvement in the growth patterns of 0–5-year-old Aboriginal children over the past 25 years. This failure has occurred despite an intensive 0–5 years' surveillance, referral and management programme based in communities throughout the region that has involved community health doctors and nurses, and Aboriginal health workers.

What is perhaps of more concern is evidence that the so-called 'lifestyle' chronic degenerative diseases are causing increasing ill-health and premature deaths in Aboriginal people. These diseases include obesity, hypertension, cardiovascular disease and type 2 diabetes mellitus. Respiratory diseases, mental disorders, injury, and poisoning are also disproportionately more prevalent and serious in the Aboriginal population – as are those diseases due to tobacco smoking and excessive alcohol consumption. Circulatory diseases have become the number one cause of deaths in Aboriginal males and females despite the fact that hypertension and cardiovascular disease were said to be rare in these people only 50 years ago. At 35–39 years (females) and 40–44 (males) mortality rates in the Aboriginal population of Western Australia are ten times those of the rest of the population; many of these excess deaths are caused by 'lifestyle' diseases, injury, and violence.

Why have the demonstrably serious inequities in health needs of the Australian Aboriginal population not been met? It can be argued that clinical services, emergency services, and some health promotion and education programmes have been provided for some of the particular needs of Aboriginal people and that some specific services, such as antenatal care, child health, nutrition, and immunisation have been targeted at high-risk groups. This has helped achieve some of the improvements cited. But why is Aboriginal health in such a dreadful state and recognised as such, both generally and by governments in Australia?

There has been a failure to develop policies that bridge the gap between provision of clinical services (disease care) and the development of effective preventive strategies and programmes (health care). Policy development, implementation and analysis have not been applied effectively to examine the precursors of ill-health in the Aboriginal population and their complexities in order to develop more appropriate, Aboriginal-oriented health policies and drive fundamental changes into the background on which Aboriginal ill-health has become so firmly entrenched. The need for effective, working links across inter-sectoral borders (governmental and non-governmental) has also been inadequately addressed. These missing links should cross such areas as health, housing, education, employment, infrastructure services and maintenance, water, sewerage, local government, and land tenure. Because poor environmental health conditions are so prevalent and have such serious negative impacts on Aboriginal health, these circumstances have to be addressed urgently before Aboriginal health improves significantly. Environmental conditions affect not only traditional public health concerns, such as intestinal parasites and infectious diseases, but have wider influences including access to nutritious and fresh food, and changes in community lifestyles.

Another major factor that has not been adequately met to date is the more effective involvement of Aboriginal people in the development and delivery of more appropriate, culturally sensitive, and acceptable health and medical services for their own people.

Aboriginal people have long advocated the view that the development of culturally appropriate health policy and services is not simply about having 'black faces' delivering non-Aboriginal health programmes, but inherently involves a re-evaluation and re-orientation of the method, content and priorities of health care and development. Such far-reaching change often challenges the traditional non-Aboriginal professional and administrative relationships and reference points. The pre-eminence of non-Aboriginal health-value judgements, roles, and priorities is regularly questioned and with increasing Aboriginal involvement in the health system, is being re-positioned. Partnerships are now being arranged between communities and Aboriginal-controlled medical services and other organisations (such as government health departments) in order to facilitate this process, which is seen by the Aboriginal population as crucial to the improvement of their health and welfare.

The appalling conditions under which Aboriginal people live are generally known and have been acknowledged by government as a national 'disgrace' and 'indictment'. The question remains, then to what extent has the health system failed Aboriginal people or how much has the general system failed them? There are so many structural impediments holding back Aboriginal health that the general system that affects their lives and welfare is inextricably involved with the ultimate outcome: health, morbidity, and mortality. The health sector in Australia must take a lead in turning this situation around so that Aboriginal health advancement becomes a reality.

Cultural differences
and historical perspectives

At the conference, Peter Brennan and Nan Carle described some of the differences between Aboriginal populations and the rest of society. Most striking were descriptions of the extent of the differences in values and historical perspectives. We cannot easily assimilate and understand these deep cultural differences. It seems we must find new ways of working across them if we are to resolve the outstanding problems. Although it has become clear that we cannot solve these problems without involving people from the other culture, it is not easy to do so.

The Minister Who Wanted To Do Something About It

The Minister of Health wanted to address the problems of Aboriginal health once and for all. He was prepared to do anything it took to solve these problems. His advisors told him that the best thing he could do would be to meet face to face with Aboriginal leaders and declare his resolve and initiate discussions. He was also sensitive to the differences in culture. His advisors told him that place was very important to the Aboriginal people, so he would do best to travel to a propitious place in their lands in order to meet. He said that he would do whatever it took and asked for the meeting to be set up.

His advisors arranged the meeting. When the minister arrived in this desolate area of the country, he was told that the Aboriginal leaders had not yet arrived. He waited for several hours and finally left, annoyed at their absence.

The next day, the Aboriginal leaders arrived and were astonished when they were told about the minister's departure. Everyone knew that the place was right and that the meeting would begin once everyone was present. It was also obvious that assembling everyone might take a few days. How rude and uncaring of the minister to depart so abruptly.

by Peter Brennan

Canada's First Nations community

Concerns about First Nations health were reinforced by a meeting with representatives of Canada's native people. There were powerful declarations about a long history of health care difficulties. And there were quiet stories about the effects of many years of failed attempts to improve the situation.

Boarding schools for Canadian native people

There have been some extreme efforts. A good example of failed well-meaning attempts to 'improve the lot of native people' was a Canadian educational effort. It was felt that the education of First Nations children would best be provided in special boarding schools where they would be free of the difficult circumstances of their home communities and without the pressures of white schools. Their training and education was meant to help them become leaders of their people and to help them to develop the First Nations communities to the level of everyone else. This effort had disastrous consequences for the young people who were separated from their families. They were then sent to alien and unfriendly schools where they felt abused, and diminished. Many then ended up alienated from their original communities as well as from the white ones.

The ethnography of the health care tribes

❦ Peter Griffiths ❧

➤ Editor's comment

It is not so clear that restructuring the system will, by itself, solve the problems of Aboriginal health. It seems as if a different approach is needed. More must be done, although it is not clear what that 'more' is. Pursuing a common set of values may not be possible, nor is there a single and obvious shared vision of the past or the future. There are some lessons here that might be applied to the rest of health care. Peter Griffiths uses an anthropological parable to summarise the extent of the divisions in health care.

This is the story of a visitor from another galaxy spending a day observing our health care system and recording what it sees as the main characteristics of the four tribes that constitute the health nation. The four tribes are the Manpols, the Three Ps, the Rots and the Youmes.

The Manpols are the managers and the politicians, the Three Ps are the professionals working for purchasers and providers, the Rots are the rest of the staff and the Youmes are you, me, our families and friends.

The Manpols
This is the tribe made up of the managers and politicians and people called non-executives who are not sure if they are either managers or politicians. The other tribes sometimes refer to the Manpols as the tribe of the 'big and little chiefs'. The Manpols' language is called SOS (which isn't short for Secretary of State), but is a language made up of Systems, Organisations and Structures. This tribe uses a currency called CAB which has two denominations called costs and benefits. The Manpols' thought-processes are interesting and unlike the rest of the tribes as they think in terms of analysis, decisions and visions. (The visions often seem like hallucinations to the other tribes.)

cont.

cont.

The Manpols dress in a particular way and the leading Pol frequently wears blue or pink and changes her hairstyle regularly for special occasions. The Mans are said to be grey-suited most of the time. The tribe has become increasingly powerful over the last ten years although their life expectancy is reducing. The Pols rarely survive longer than five years and the Mans for even shorter periods of time now at an average life expectancy of three years with 30 per cent of them disappearing every year. The Manpols have an interesting definition of listening which is what they do when they are waiting to make their own point – which is why they enjoy something called debate most of the time when they can simply promote their own view.

The tribe is not very popular amongst the other tribes, but that doesn't worry them too much as they know what is right and necessary for the others. However, this changes every now and then when things called elections and contract reviews take place. The Manpols are regarded by the other tribes as always getting things right, usually having exhausted all other possibilities first. Members of the tribe are easily spotted because they use mobile phones, fax machines, and computers, and drive things called leased cars. The most senior Mans spend much of their time on trains between places called Leeds and London.

The Manpols have an interesting approach to relaxation which is to work even more at evenings and weekends and they are therefore, a very intense and earnest tribe who often bore their partners and the other tribes rigid. The tribe forms into groups for self-protection which they call political parties or institutes and associations. The Manpols used to work very closely with the Three Ps to help convince the Youmes that what they said was right because the Three Ps are still trusted more by the Youmes than are the Manpols. The Manpols are becoming increasingly dispirited because the other tribes don't seem to appreciate that what is being proposed for them is good.

The Three Ps
This is the tribe of the professionals who work for providers and purchasers and are sometimes known by the other tribes as the 'white coats'. Their language is called DOP which is a language made up of diseases and populations. Their currency is called ITO which has three denominations called investigations, treatments, and outcomes. The Three Ps think in terms of scientific enquiry, logic, and controlled trials. The tribe has always been very influential with the Youmes but that appears to be changing as the Youmes attend more and more assertiveness training courses.

Many of the Three Ps don't like the Manpols who keep on asking what the Three Ps are really doing and what difference it makes. The Three Ps are the most educated of the tribes and go to the best schools and obtain a lot of things called qualifications which allow them to know that what they do is always right.

cont.

cont.

Members of The Three Ps tribe are the best networkers of all the tribes and spend much time travelling from one country to another to learn from each other and see nice places. Three Ps have quite long life-spans and can survive for 20 years or more.

For self-protection, they too form into groups which they call Royal Colleges and Associations. The Three Ps have things called medical schools and colleges of nursing that enable them to reproduce Three Ps in exactly the same form time after time after time. The tribe is driven by wanting to make individual Youmes and whole populations of Youmes better. In order to do this, they organise them into things called diagnostic and socio-economic groups. Many of the Three Ps work in places called institutions which allows them to protect themselves from where the Youmes live. The tribe is currently confused because there are those who want to continue working in the institutions which are becoming fewer, and those who want to work in a place called the community where the Youmes actually live.

The Rots

This is the tribe made up by the rest of the staff and are sometimes called the 'non-Core tribe'. Their language is PASS and is made up of practical and supporting services. Their currency is JAS which has two denominations called jobs and security. They are the most numerous of the tribes with the exception of the Youmes, although their numbers have decreased significantly over recent years as a result of them being affected by a rampant disease called contracting out. The Rots have most in common with the Youmes as they speak their language and often interpret what the Three Ps are saying for the Youmes. They are often called the invisible people because the Manpols and the Three Ps seem not to recognise them much.

The Rots seem to be more subject to something called 'downsizing' than the Manpols and the Three Ps, but get a lot of help with after-care called 'outplacement'. The tribe is subject to something called monitoring by the Manpols because it is assumed that they are naturally weaker and more subject to suffering from sickness and absence. Some of the Rots are still expected to do something called clocking in and clocking out because it is assumed that otherwise they will get lost. The Rots are given much training and supervision in case they are unable to use their own discretion in solving problems.

The Youmes

This is the tribe of you, me, our friends and families, and are sometimes called the tribe of the 'done tos'. They are the most numerous of all the tribes and their population swells at night and on weekends when the Three Ps, the Rots and the Manpols become Youmes.

cont.

cont.

The other tribes owe their allegiance to the Youmes who pay all their bills, but somehow it doesn't seem like that to the Youmes. Their language is WAN which is wants and needs. Their currency is CAS which is made up of denominations of care and support. They think in terms of emotions and feelings.

The Youmes often accompany the other tribes to conferences as partners and have special events organised for them because they wouldn't understand what the other tribes are up to. The Youmes are a very hospitable tribe and socialise a great deal at their own expense whilst the other tribes network at the Youmes' expense. The tribe receives much of their information not by the kind of papers that the other tribes produce, but by their own papers called newspapers. The Youmes are very frustrating to the other tribes because they don't always do what they are told or what is good for them. They often like drinking and smoking and eating food with salt in it.

The Youmes have some difficulty in communicating with the other tribes and sometimes use different words which start with F or B or S. This causes particular concern to the Three Ps at times called consultations. The Youmes also organise into groups for self-protection called Families and Friendly Societies. The Youmes are told it is good for them not to use the services of the other tribes as they are very expensive and it would be better for them to stay healthy and look after themselves as long as they still pay the same level of taxes. The Youmes are particularly concerned about entering the Three Ps' institutions as they will be counted as discharges, deaths, or finished episodes.

What are the central and more serious messages to be taken from this humorous galactic observer's story?

That despite our success in improving the performance of the health care system, the gap between the managed and managers remains wide and may be growing. We managers are seen to be a different tribe and more aligned with our political masters than representing the interests of our employees and local communities. There is a significant issue about the language we use adding to the feeling of distance between us and our major partners. There is also an issue to be addressed about the short-term duration of managers, particularly those in senior positions who are leading and promoting significant change agendas. A recent survey by the IHSM (the British health managers' association) showed that only 6 per cent of managers had been in their positions for four years or more.

There is a perception that we regard our most cherished asset, the people who work with us, as being as disposable and dispensable as buildings and equipment. One of the consequences of our inevitable and necessary focus on structure, systems, and costs over the last few years has been to create the impression that we are losing sight of the essential purposes of health care. Whilst opportunities for creating new and exciting partnerships between managers and professionals in primary and community care are emerging, there is some evidence that these essential partnerships in the hospital sector are becoming more and more strained.

Editor's comment

Peter Griffiths' comic allegory suggests that many of the splits inside health care might be 'cultural'. That is, that they have to do with different perceptions, values and experiences of the many participants in the worlds of health care. There is evidence to suggest that some of the differences are of long standing and have persisted through many attempts at change and reform. Many of the participants carry a history of misunderstanding, suspicion and mistrust of others. It is not surprising that there should be differences of cultural magnitude between the different professional groups in health care. The intractability of the problems associated with Aboriginal health seem matched by the intractability of the divisions in health care.

A study examining journals of two medical residents 'written more than 100 years apart ... revealed more similarities than differences in nurse-doctor relationships'. The two groups have worked in intimate proximity for the past hundred years, but the difficulties in their relationship have not been significantly reduced despite numerous restructuring efforts. The split between them is not only a war of the sexes, status and pay; it has many other dimensions including differences in education, attitude and values. It is also about who controls hospitals. A book on the history of nursing summarises the situation:

> For the last hundred years the general hospital has been the key battleground for the various forces arrayed in the division of labour in health care. There132 seems no reason this should change now.
> (Dingwall, 1988)

There are similar differences that occur between different parts of health care systems. The relationship between doctors and nurses is mirrored by that between acute hospitals and community-based services. And just as all structural efforts to resolve inter-professional rivalry have failed, so have the structural solutions that have been imposed on health care systems.

The limits of simple fixes

&- Robert J Maxwell -&

Editor's comment

Through an examination of different moments in the history of the NHS, Robert Maxwell critically assesses the integral changes and identifies the key players, influential documents and policies which assisted in making this health care system what it is now.

He outlines the first step in the reorganisation process as one which led to the division of England into regions by area and district. Some regions had management at both the district and area levels offering some opportunities and integrated programmes, while there were other organisations whose experiences proved the restructuring to have had its drawbacks, especially a cumbersome structure.

Further moves to change the focus to a more patient-centred structure in the early-1980s, which threw most senior managers throughout the system into a tail-spin, concerned for their jobs. The result was another survey into the workings of the NHS carried out by Roy Griffiths, proposing a more streamlined structure which would concentrate on heavy leadership while linking existing mechanisms efficiently. A final spin occurred in 1988 with the release of a closed-doors assessment called 'Working for Patients', a right-wing option of managed care, full of purchasers and GP fund-holders.

Maxwell reflects on the various attempts at restructuring the NHS. Firstly, the constant striving to find the perfect structure may be wrong, he says. There will always be trade-offs to each structure suggested, and perhaps more importantly, the people who make up the organisation will be the true test of whether or not it is 'successful': 'organisations are only as good as the people in them'. Since politicians are those who have determined these changes in structure, they are often only carried out as long as one party is in power; in other words, long-term, well-thought out plans are not the ones which are implemented, rather the quick fix is preferred.

Maxwell calls for governments to be participants in the process of developing a health care structure but urges them to allow the micro-operational dealings to be handled by the implementers. He says that massive and constant changes will only lead to confusion and detract from the essence of the programme: actual implementation.

The case-study in this paper concerns the National Health Service, but (I will argue) it also has relevance for countries other than the UK. When the NHS was set up under the NHS Act of 1946, the organisational form that was chosen for it was in some ways radical, but in others perpetuated the arrangements of the past. The radical bit was the nationalisation of the voluntary hospitals. The cautious part (reflected in Figure 1) was to have four separate organisational strands, representing public health and community health services (which remained under local government control), family practitioner services (under executive councils, stemming ultimately from the insurance committees set up under the National Health Insurance Act of 1911), the non-teaching hospitals (under Hospital Management Committees of the new Regional Hospital Boards) and the teaching hospitals (with their own Boards of Governors, answering directly to the Minister).

There was little merit in this organisation, which meant that nobody short of ministers and their most senior advisers dealt with all aspects of the NHS, even in a single locality. But it survived intact until 1974 – in other words for quarter of a century, or more than half the history of the NHS from its beginnings until the present. In 1968, however, when Kenneth Robinson was Minister of Health, he published a Green Paper[1] proposing the integration of all these strands under Area Boards, which would correspond geographically to local government boundaries. In 1968, Richard Crossman, as Secretary of State for Social Services, proposed a variant to these arrangements in a Second Green Paper.[2] The Labour government then fell and the task of deciding on a new organisation for the National Health Service passed to Sir Keith Joseph, the incoming Conservative Secretary of State.

Case study: round 1

Later, Sir Keith, in his Thatcherite mode, was to become extremely penitent about the cumbersome, ornate management arrangements which he was responsible for inflicting on the NHS via what came to be called the Grey Book.[3] This report was overseen by a large steering committee comprising people from the NHS and from the Department of Health and Social Security, chaired by the then civil servant head of the Department, Sir Philip Rogers. Under the steering committee was a study group, assisted by a team from the Health Services Organisation Research Unit at Brunel University and from McKinsey and Company, management consultants.*

---

* At this point I first became personally involved in the story as I was working for McKinsey and Company at the time and was their health specialist, having worked on health service reorganisation in New York and the Republic of Ireland among other things. I was not a member of the NHS study team because I was working on a separate reorganisation of the Department of Health, but I was sufficiently close to the NHS work to have a fair knowledge of it.

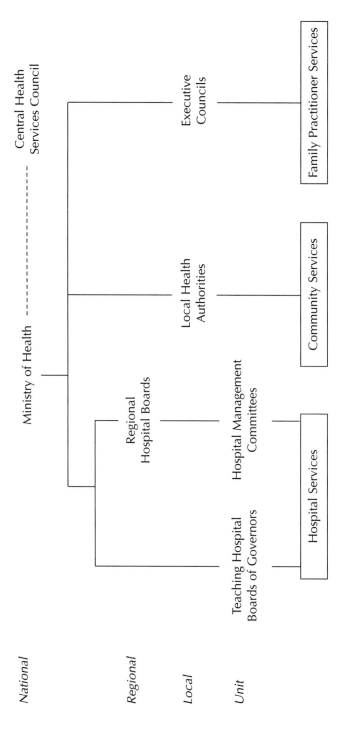

Figure 1 The National Health Service 1948–74

Source: Levitt, R, & Wall, A. *The Reorganised National Health Service.* London: Chapman & Hall, 1992 (4th edition)

The Grey Book is the most detailed management blueprint ever published for the National Health Service. It defines its organisation and the nature of the relationships between the levels (*see Figure 2*), the functions and organisation at each level, all the main job specifications in the structure, and the management processes (planning, monitoring and control, and personnel management) that were to be used. While the status of the Grey Book was a report to the Secretary of State, which he would accept or reject, in fact it became the management bible of the 1974 Reorganisation, in standard form throughout the National Health Service in England, and substantially in Wales. There was more variation in Scotland and in Northern Ireland.

In later years, the Grey Book has come to be seen as a high-water mark of the discredited structural approach to management that had already had its heyday in British business a decade earlier. But it was actually a good deal more complicated than that. The detailed differentiation of roles and relationships owed a lot to Brunel's research in the National Health Service, led by Professor Eliot Jacques and his colleague Ralph Rowbottom,[4] and reflected some of the particular complexities of hospitals, including the nature of professional hierarchies and inter-disciplinary tensions. Some of the resulting classifications may be over elaborate, almost botanical, but they are peculiar to the health field, not imported into it. Moreover, the nature and the composition of the steering committee meant that it was a forum for negotiation, and that some of the negotiations went on elsewhere. For example, the notion of a District Management Team comprising community physician, nurse, finance officer and administrator, plus two elected medical representatives, all functioning by consensus, is one that owed something to Brunel, but considerably more to negotiation outside and inside the steering committee. Another example was the decision (not taken within the steering committee) to have both districts and areas. My impression is that that came as a device to reconcile two different, strongly held ideas: first, that NHS and local government structures should correspond at the area level, and second, that a unit of NHS organisation should be the district of roughly 250,000 people, because that was the natural catchment area for a District General Hospital (DGH) and hence was the first level at which all local NHS services could be integrated managerially. In rather more than a third of NHS areas in England and Wales the two ideas came together, because the local authority's population was small enough to correspond to a hospital district in what came to be called the single-district areas. But in roughly two-thirds of areas (comprising 80 per cent of districts) this was not the case: hence there were to be management teams at both district and area levels. (There was also strong advocacy for the continuation of regions in England, on the grounds that they formed a sensible unit for planning tertiary services and that there were, in any case, too many areas to be dealt with directly by national government.)

The implementation date for the Grey Book reorganisation was 1 April 1974. Ironically, Edward Heath's Conservative government fell in February, so the task of

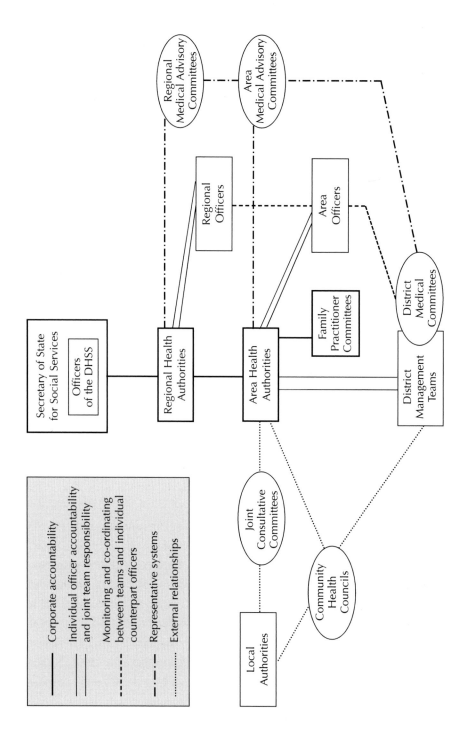

Figure 2 The NHS Reorganisation of 1974

Source: DHSS. *Management Arrangements for the Reorganised National Health Service.* London: HMSO, 1972

presiding over the reorganisation switched back to a Labour government, with Barbara Castle as Secretary of State. The new government considered whether to view the whole matter, but in the event let the reorganisation go ahead, introducing only relatively minor modifications in the name of strengthening local accountability.[5] Community Health Councils (CHCs) were given certain limited statutory powers, the new health authorities were to meet in public, and a proportion of their members were to be nominated by the local authorities from among their own elected members.

In the event the new organisation took about two years to settle down. It turned out to have both strengths and weaknesses. Among the strengths was – as had been hoped – the concept of an integrated district, with the opportunity and the incentive to allocate money across traditional service boundaries. Not that the opportunities were always taken, partly because the integration of family practitioner services under Area Health Authorities was more theoretical than real: they retained their own separate administration and were separately funded from the national level with allocations that were open-ended and outside the main NHS budgets. Nevertheless, the existence of defined NHS districts did prompt attempts to define needs and the impact of services on the basis of population studies, rather than assumptions. Clinicians and managers who wanted to work across the traditional separation between hospital and community-based services were encouraged to do so.

On the other hand the new organisation proved in some ways cumbersome. Decision-making processes could be slow because of the elaboration of the structure and the heavy emphasis on consultation and consensus. The strength of management at the hospital level tended to be eroded as administrators saw the new jobs at district level as their path to the top. Probably the most widely voiced criticism was (as one might have foreseen) that there was one tier too many in the new structure. On the whole, the single district areas seemed to work better than the multi-district areas, where there could be substantial tensions between the two levels.

This dissatisfaction with some aspects of the 1974 reorganisation was a factor (though certainly not the only one) in prompting Harold Wilson in 1976 to nominate a Royal Commission on the National Health Service to examine the best use of its financial and manpower resources. Wilson was adept at the use of Royal Commissions as a diversionary device, so the fact that the Commission reported after the general election of 1979 was no accident. Granted the profound seismic shift away from consensus politics represented by the arrival of Mrs Margaret Thatcher at No.10 Downing Street, it was inevitable that the Royal Commission's report[6] would have limited relevance to anything she would decide to do. For what it is worth, however, the Royal Commission did in fact conclude that the organisation of the NHS was over-elaborate and that one tier should be removed in most places. The Commission also wished to abolish family practitioner committees.

Case study: round 2

Mrs Thatcher became Prime Minister in May 1979. In December, a slim consultation paper *Patients First*,[7] on the structure and management of the NHS in England and Wales, was published by the new government – chiefly, it seems, as a response to the Royal Commission report. It proposed the abolition of the area tier and the establishment of health authorities at district level.

In effect this meant that the single-district areas of 1974 would survive in most cases, while the multi-district areas would be split up. Hence the number of health authorities would increase sharply, and conterminosity on a one-to-one basis between health and local government would generally be lost.

The consultation paper considered, but rejected, a number of ideas for more radical change discussed by the Royal Commission. These included the idea that regional health authorities might become directly accountable to parliament; the abolition of family practitioner committees; transferring responsibility for the NHS to local government, or for social services to the health authorities; and the replacement of management teams by individual chief executives. Apart from the abolition of areas and the establishment of health authorities at the district level, professional advisory machinery was to be simplified, as was the planning system. There should be maximum delegation of management responsibility to the local level – a familiar slogan of every NHS reorganisation.

The reorganisation based on *Patients First* was implemented following legislation, from 1 April 1982, with consequential changes spread over the next 18 months. The intention was to avoid the turbulence of the 1974 reorganisation, but in practice the management turbulence was great as virtually every senior job was affected. It was like a game of musical chairs, in which people feared to find themselves without a post when the music stopped.

Case study: round 3

Almost before this game had ended, another management inquiry had been set up. Norman Fowler, as Secretary of State, had asked Roy Griffiths, Managing Director of Sainsbury's, to advise on 'the effective use and management of manpower and related resources' in the NHS. What lay behind this request was an increasing restiveness on the part of the Cabinet generally and Mrs Thatcher in particular, at the capacity of the NHS to absorb real increases in funding, and then to come back to ask for more. Norman Fowler had an unusually long period as Secretary of State for Social Services, from 1981 to 1987. He was adept at negotiation with the Treasury and at astute manoeuvring to avoid confrontation within the Social Services. The remit to Roy Griffiths was a way (following the government's re-election in 1983) to expose the inner managerial workings of the NHS to the scrutiny of a group of businessmen, who would not be easily fobbed off with bureaucratic or wimpish social welfare excuses. The Prime Minister herself had confidence in him. She was not seeking a public confrontation on the NHS, which was not then at the top of her hit list for the radical reform of Britain, but equally she thought what was needed was a good hard external look at its efficiency.

The inquiry was completed in approximately six months. The resulting brief report[8] criticised the diffusion of management responsibility in the NHS ('if Florence Nightingale were carrying her lamp through the corridors of the NHS today she would almost certainly be searching for the people in charge') and the lack of a clearly defined focus and drive for the planning, implementation and control of performance ('the NHS is so structured as to resemble a "mobile": designed to move with any breath of air, but which in fact never changes its position and gives no clear indication of direction').

Griffiths recommended the creation of a single general management line to run from the Secretary of State at the centre to individuals in charge at the operational (for example, hospital) level. The Secretary of State would chair a Health Services Supervisory Board below which there would be a Management Board charged with heading the general management process in the NHS. Its chairman would be an experienced executive, probably drawn from outside central government and the NHS – in short someone like Roy Griffiths himself. From the Management Board outwards there would be a single general manager at each level: region, district, unit. While no attempt was made to remove the regional and district health authorities, they were urged to clarify what decisions they would reserve to themselves and what should be done on their behalf by the general manager and chief officers. In essence the task at the centre was to set the direction for the NHS, not simply in intellectual terms but in terms of energy and leadership; the task at unit level was to achieve change and maximise performance, in partnership with the clinicians; in between centre and unit were the link mechanisms, to convey direction, protect and support local managerial autonomy, and hold to account.

The Griffiths report met with a hostile response, particularly from the professions.*

---

* I was asked by Cliff Graham, chief of staff to the inquiry, to host a dinner to discuss the conclusions at the draft stage. It quickly became clear that this was more a selling than a consultation exercise. At that time I felt that Sir Roy (as he later became) had under-estimated the strength of the case for interdisciplinary management teams in the NHS and I wanted the approach to change to be more experimental, less mandatory. Not for the last time in the context of this case study, I lost that argument. Once the Secretary of State had accepted the Griffiths report, I sought, in conjunction with my colleague, the late Tom Evans, to persuade all those involved in the NHS to grasp the opportunity presented by Griffiths' recommendations and show what the NHS could do with them. In particular we stressed the possibility of combining central strategic direction with a truly decentralised operational management of health services.[9]

Despite this opposition, the report was quickly accepted by the Secretary of State, with a view to immediate implementation.

Once again, like the 1982 reorganisation, the game of musical chairs followed as, at all levels, people competed for general manager jobs. A few went to the professions, and some to candidates from business, local government, and the armed forces. Most, however, went to what had previously been called NHS administrators, who found themselves in more powerful positions than ever before, but positions that were also more politically exposed. Nursing found itself in disarray, as a result of the virtual annihilation of nursing management. The medical profession did not know quite what to make of it all.

Case study: round 4

The Griffiths recommendations, with their accent on building a general management process and culture, were designed for the long-term. Their impact continues ten years later and their force is still by no means spent. But they did not provide any immediate resolution to the problems of financing the NHS. Once again, in the run-up to the 1987 general election, the Conservative manifesto did not major on the National Health Service. 'The NHS is safe in our hands,' countered Mrs Thatcher to allegations by the Labour party that her government could not be trusted on this issue.

The Conservatives were re-elected, winning for the third time in succession, but within months the government was subject to an unprecedented public attack by the Presidents of the three premier Royal Colleges that the NHS was falling apart for lack of money. Mrs Thatcher countered with the argument that year-by-year expenditure on the NHS had increased in real terms. Although this was true (at least on one set of assumptions) it did not feel like the truth to many of those working in the NHS, nor to the general public. Among the reasons was the fact that increases in salary and wage costs were determined nationally and were funded only on the assumption of efficiency savings that had to be achieved by the health authorities. Moreover, the position was much worse in places like London, which were at the same time losing money under resource redistribution policies, designed to achieve greater fairness between north and south.

The statement by the College Presidents in early December 1987 struck a chord of public response. Day by day and week by week the funding of the National Health Service was headline news: as so often individual cases were used (with incomplete facts) to illustrate the impact of rationing. The Opposition called for an independent inquiry, or Royal Commission. Mrs Thatcher, forced on the defensive, ultimately yielded a governmental review, to be led by herself. She was – and remained – angry at being wrong-footed, and resentful at the influence exerted by the profession, in the persons of the Royal College Presidents.

Her review took place in the calendar year 1988, behind closed doors. For some time even the composition of her review team was unknown, and it was never formally announced. (It included, besides herself, the Chancellor of the Exchequer, the Secretary of State for Social Services and their next in-line Ministers). No public evidence was taken.* A certain amount of information leaked out about the topics considered and the stage reached: for example, that a switch from general taxation to insurance-based funding was considered and rejected. Late in the day John Moore, the Secretary of State for Social Services, who had not been a great success in the post, was replaced by Kenneth Clarke (previously Minister of State), who appeared to have a particularly strong influence on the ultimate conclusions. These conclusions were published in January 1989, under the title *Working for Patients*.[10]

Working for Patients is a very uneven document. It contains what it describes as 'seven key changes', but these range from the modestly incremental (one half of one extra hospital consultant post per district) and the barely controversial (medical audit) to the truly radical (self-governing status for hospitals and some form of competition among providers). Two of the most important ideas – the NHS district as the key unit for purchasing and GP fund-holders as purchasers – had different intellectual parentages and seemed bound to be mutually incompatible in the long-term. Thus the NHS Reforms, as they were called by their progenitors, were something of an intellectual hotchpotch. Nevertheless, it would be wrong to view them as a cynical attempt to undermine the NHS, as hostile critics alleged. My own view was, and is, that they comprised an assortment of right wing radical ideas intended to reconcile the virtues of a collective National Health Service with the encouragement of enterprise through the workings of a managed market. These ideas may or may not prove beneficial. That is an empirical, not an ideological question. But I see no reason to impugn the integrity of those who promulgated them.

The implementation of changes began in April 1990. From a political viewpoint the timing was bad. With a general election likely in 1991, what people would remember at election time would be the controversy and disturbance associated with the changes. A period of about 12 months would be too short to demonstrate benefits. Hence the strong directive from the NHS Management Executive (as Sir Roy Griffiths' Management Board had become) down through the NHS was that managers should hasten slowly.

---

* There appeared to be two routes by which ideas could be fed into the review. One was from the right-wing policy think tanks, the other the Department of Health. Perhaps the Treasury was a third. In my experience (using the Department of Health route) one did not hear what the reaction had been. Along, no doubt, with many others, I sought to persuade the protagonists of the merits of pilot projects. The idea did not appeal, nor later did the suggestion that the changes that resulted from the review should be systematically evaluated.

In the event the government was re-elected for a fourth term. Had the opposition won, the Thatcher NHS Reforms, reflected in the present NHS structure shown in Figure 3, would have been reversed. As it is, the process of implementation is continuing. To date, the jury is still out on the net impact of the changes. The most comprehensive assessment yet published[11] is by no means conclusive, partly because of the complexity of the research task and partly because it is still early days. Some observations, however, can be made. For example, transaction costs have risen, as a result of the new management structures and the additional information required by the new system. On the other hand, cost information has improved sharply. In terms of service quality, the patients of GP fund-holders, in particular, have benefited from shorter waiting times and better feedback of information to their GPs, but at the expense of equity, since gaps have opened between them and other patients. The maxim that, in the new system, money would follow the patient may be true for the patients of GP fund-holders. For others it seems more true that patients have to go where the contracts say they should. Extra-contractual referrals (i.e. referrals outside the main contracts) can create substantial tensions and are much less straightforward than cross-boundary referrals used to be under the old system.

In the main it is simply too soon to give a balanced verdict. Hospital and Community Trusts have greater autonomy on paper than their predecessors. Will this autonomy be eroded over the years? Will it prove beneficial? How real will competition among providers prove to be, and will it deliver benefits? Will the initial weaknesses in purchasing be overcome? What *modus vivendi* will be achieved between districts as purchasers and GP fund-holders?

What does seem likely is that, if there is a change of the party in power at the next election, something will survive. It probably will not be GP fund-holding. It may be a degree of managerial autonomy for providers, though the composition of their boards will change. It is quite likely to be, in some form, a continued differentiation between the commissioning of services and their provision. There seems now to be a general acceptance that government's task is more about ensuring the provision of services then it is about providing them, and that direct responsibility for provision can at times weight the scales too much towards the perpetuation of existing services and institutions.

Reflections on the case

Perhaps the best starting point for reflection (in true Kleinian spirit) is a paradox. Each of the changes divided in the four rounds of the case study had some justification, and each has left some benefits, but overall it is highly questionable whether they have been worthwhile. Let us explore the paradox further and then ask what advice, based on the case study, one would give governments for the future.

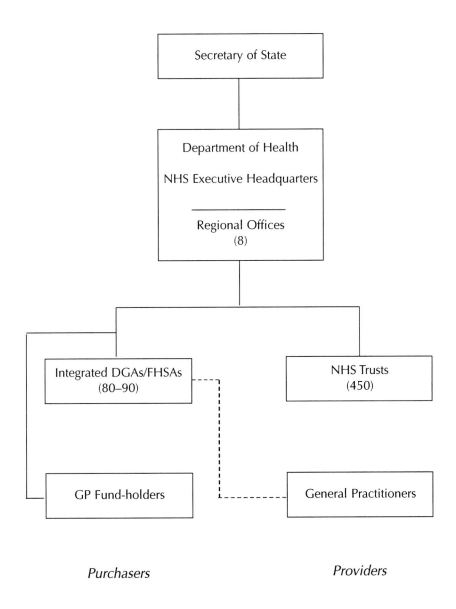

Figure 3 The new structure of the NHS

Source: Department of Health. *Managing the New NHS*. London: DoH, 1993

Organisation is important, but not all-important and there is probably no such thing as organisational perfection

In *Patients First*, the apparently reasonable proposition is put forward that 'It is fundamental to making a national health service work well in response to patients' needs that the structure and management of the service should be right.'[12] But what does 'right' mean in this context? There is no doubt that organisations can get in the way of human action: for example, working across organisational boundaries is always difficult, whether the boundaries are those between government departments, or between health and social services. Nevertheless organisations are simply frameworks that are more or less well-tailored to the work to be done within them at the time. How well they function is an empirical question, rather than a theoretical one, so anybody whose field is organisational design would be wise to test the design in action.

It is highly unlikely that there is any such thing as a perfect organisation for several reasons. For example, there are often trade-offs to be made – in the context of the case-study the trade-offs between, among other things, the merits of conterminosity with local government versus the merits of the district as a natural hospital catchment area. Moreover, the management agenda faced by an institution or agency changes sharply over time and it would be strange if this did not need to be reflected in organisational adaptation. Finally, organisations are only as good as the people in them, their morale and their commitment. Ultimately, people can make any organisation work, while there is no organisational framework that can substitute for demoralised people.

Organisational forms are not ideologically neutral. People who hold differing views, for example about the respective roles of professionals and managers, or about authority and accountability, will have sharply divergent views on what is 'right' in organisational teams. One can see clearly that a future Labour government would find it almost impossible not to change Mrs Thatcher's market-driven organisational model. While a case could be made for each of the rounds of change described in this case study, and something remains from each, none resulted in a perfect organisation, nor is there any likelihood that such a state will ever be reached.

Governments work to short time horizons and they like quick fixes

In the UK, the maximum life time of a government is five years. More typically it is four, so that the party in power can pick its moment to go to the polls. The average period for any politician in any one office, such as the Secretary of State for Health, is more likely two-and-a-half years. These political realities affect the thinking and the behaviour of virtually every minister and every government. Faced with a complex, chronic problem, they are seldom attracted to complex, long-term solutions. What they must have is an action that can be taken relatively fast, and preferably one that will show a political return before the next election. Organisational change has too often seemed to meet these requirements. But whatever the real problems of the NHS are (and we will come to that in a moment) they are not of a kind that are resolved by a quick fix.

Whatever the merits of large-scale organisational change, it carries a high price-tag in terms of its impact on people, particularly if it is done repeatedly

The initial organisation of the NHS – imperfect as it was – lasted from 1948 to 1974. Since then the Service has been subject to repeated reorganisations, at shorter and shorter intervals. It seems as though the NHS is always contemplating reorganisation, or undergoing it, or recovering.

When I first came across Petronius' classic comment on this subject in the Satyricon, I was amused by its aptness. I am no longer so amused. The words describe only too clearly the state of mind of those who have been continually reorganised.*

One effect of constant NHS reorganisations has been to occupy the attention of senior managers and politicians, and distract them from what the NHS is actually about

There is a real danger that the institutional leadership of the NHS is busy with an agenda that neither most of those working in it nor the public understand. In the period from, say, the publication of **Working for Patients** in January 1989 until now, what proportion of the time and energy of health ministers and NHS senior managers has gone into the actual problems of delivering services to patients, compared with (in its broadest sense) structural change and its implications? It is almost as though senior management and the politicians were detached from the reality of what they are there to lead, and contribute virtually nothing to the service from day to day.

So, what is the real problem to which organisational change has been the symptomatic response rather than the solution?

The heart of the matter is about finding and allocating the resources for health care in a situation where the gap continually widens between expectations and what is available. It can be variously expressed as achieving excellence within tight constraints, or obtaining value for money, or balancing aims that pull in different directions. It is a wicked rather than a tame problem in the sense that it has no neat or permanent solution.

Government has to be a participant (not only in the UK but everywhere) because of the importance of health and the scale of public resources committed to it. But

---

*'We trained hard – but it seemed that every time we were beginning to form up into teams we would be reorganised. I was to learn later in life that we tend to meet any new situation by reorganising, and a wonderful method it can be for creating the illusion of progress while producing confusion, inefficiency and demoralisation.'

From Petronius, *The Satyricon*, c.AD 65

there is no way in which government can itself handle the detailed, day-to-day issues, nor fix them in a way that stays fixed. As an OECD publication, *The Reform of Health Care*,[13] suggests, based on a comparative analysis of seven OECD countries, it may be useful to differentiate between on the one hand setting the framework for tackling these issues and on the other tackling them in a micro or operational sense. Government can do the first; it cannot do the second and is unwise to try.

Conclusion

In conclusion, the advice to governments based on this case study might be, first, to be as specific as possible about the problems they are trying to solve, rather than reaching too quickly for solutions. Second, to try to resist the temptation to make repeated massive systems changes, whether these are organisational or process, and to reorganise the price of repeated change in terms of morale. Third, to take a more evolutionary approach, with a greater respect for evidence, than is shown in this case study. All the indications are that no intervention on the scale of any of the rounds in this case produces precisely what is intended. Whether or not one accepts the argument for piloting change, one should in a broader sense see change as a learning process where it is in everyone's interest to assess effects before anyone intervenes again. Gardening is quite a good analogy for management: continually digging up the plants, to re-examine their roots and move them around, is not a good way to establish a flourishing National Health Service.

References

1. Ministry of Health, *The Administrative Structure of Medical and Related Services in England and Wales*. London: HMSO, 1990.
2. DHSS, *The Future Structure of the National Health Service*. London: HMSO, 1970.
3. DHSS. *Management Arrangements for the Reorganised National Health Service*. London: HMSO, 1972.
4. Rowbottom, R. *Hospital Organisation: A Progress Report on the Brunel Health Services Organisation Project*. London: Heinemann, 1973.
5. DHSS, *Democracy in the National Health Service*. London: HMSO, 1974.
6. Royal Commission on the National Health Service, *Report*. Chairman: Sir Alex Merrison. London: HMSO, 1979 (Command 7615).
7. DHSS and Welsh Office, *Patients First*. London: HMSO, 1979.
8. NHS Management Inquiry, *Report*. Chairman: Roy Griffiths. London: DHSS, 1983.
9. Evans, T, Maxwell, R. *Griffiths: Challenge and Response*. London: King's Fund, 1984.
10. Department of Health. *Working for Patients*. London: HMSO, 1989.
11. Robinson, R, Le Grand, J. *Evaluating the NHS Reforms*. London: King's Fund Institute, 1994.
12. *op cit* (7 above).
13. OECD, *The Reform of Health Care: A Comparative Analysis of Seven OECD Countries*. Paris: Health Policy Studies No. 2, OECD 1992.

3 Some ways forward

Part 3 presents an evaluation of:

- *the essential role of universities/medical schools in physician resource planning*

- *health sector reform in South Africa and the development of a distinct health system*

- *not-for-profit providers and network development*

We no longer believe that if only we could get the structures of our health care systems right, everything else would follow. We used to think that if we could only re-organise the system to get rid of the perverse incentives, the well-protected enclaves, the self-serving empires, we could reduce, if not eliminate, most of the conflict, inefficiency, duplication and gaps. Appropriate incentives could motivate providers, managed competition could provide energy, independent self-controlled institutions could have proper loyalties, collaborative agencies could provide seamless care, and so on.

The post-reform environment suggests that structural reform alone cannot be the answer. The splits that existed before restructuring are often merely submerged only to re-appear in a different guise. A good example has been the introduction of programme-based hospitals which substitute multi-disciplinary programmes for the old silos and chimneys of the disciplines. After great efforts to manage this change, new boundaries quickly appear when the vertical chimneys turn into horizontal sewer pipes.

It also seems that for all the restructuring, the internal fragmentation between some of the professions on the provider side has not been diminished. The struggle between doctors and nurses has so far not been resolved by changing organisational structures. There is little chance that there is a structure in which these differences would magically disappear.

In the last several days of the conference, members began to explore some non-structural solutions to the problems of health care. Tom Rundel described the development of the network of organisations and agencies dealing with AIDS. The difficulties and successes of this network helped to illustrate some of the main lessons of the conference.

Who are the players?

In the health care organisation of 1935, roles were very clear: one was a patient or a doctor or a nurse. This clarity has gradually eroded as the boundaries of care and role descriptions become more fuzzy. Even identifying who plays a role has become more difficult. It is harder to know who is an appropriate participant in planning, managing, or delivering health care. In fact the range of participants seems to be changing continually, and many who are not even considered by the usual players can be most critical to the success or failure of some efforts. The participants in the AIDS example were members of a variety of different voluntary, government, and community agencies as well as groups including patients, care givers, doctors, nurses and administrators. Some of them were not initially known to others.

In this last section of the book, Sarah Prichard presents a case for the close involvement of medical schools in medical human resource planning at the system level. She also suggests that their involvement not only makes a difference but may be necessary for the successful management of medical human resource development and distribution.

How can they work together?

In 1935, when there were clearer lines of authority, the decisions of one person were the final word. In many hospitals the medical superintendent was in charge. There was no need or inclination to consider other views. Today there are many individuals and groups over whom there is no such authority; whoever the participants are, they often do not share values, or visions, or interests. They must still find ways of working together.

The groups who joined up to co-ordinate the support for people with AIDS were made up of representatives of diverse communities, with differing sets of attitudes. What brought them together was a concern about AIDS that helped them develop a shared agenda despite their many differences.

Tim Wilson describes the emergence of health care plans in South Africa where a shared agenda can bring together participants with different values and perspectives.

What might the structures look like?

It is becoming more and more difficult to identify and manage the boundaries of health care organisations. This means that management's understanding must extend beyond the parameters of one's own organisation as must the clinical work. This is a major change from the organisation of 1935 where the limits of the hospital were well identified and quite rigid: one was either in or out of the hospital. As the boundaries of the problems shift, the organisations that respond to them change as well. Different organisations need not create a single governance structure in order to share an agenda.

In the AIDS example, the agencies that worked together were linked for the AIDS cause, and as time went on, some were added while others dropped out. A loose affiliation such as this, carries with it difficulty and uncertainty.

In the last essay, Fred Alley describes the advantages and difficulties of a network of providers forming the basis of integrated health care.

The essential role of universities (medical schools) in physician resource planning

✥ Sarah Prichard ✥

✏ Editor's comment

Sarah Prichard examines the technique of physician resource planning, which is used as a means to increase accessibility to health care and also to reduce health care expenditures. She assesses how this process can affect several different constituencies in general, and then looks specifically at the case of Quebec.

In order to decrease the number of physicians in Quebec, enrolment in medical schools has become severely regulated, both in number and in accepted regional origin. Non-Quebec Canadians are expected to sign an agreement stating they will not practice inside Quebec upon graduation. Better physician distribution has been encouraged through financial and educational incentives.

Sarah Prichard insists that success in implementing physician resource planning in Quebec began only after the deans of university medical schools and their associates became involved in the planning. They are able to pave the way for these reforms and prepare medical students for the changes. They can provide the educational incentives for improving resource distribution and so on. She argues that involving others in the planning process can be an essential step. There must be a recognition that critical players must include more than the traditional ministry/provider loop.

Health care reform in Canada is aimed at delivering the most effective health care programmes to the population within a budget that is bearable to the taxpayer. Canadians also wish to maintain a single payor, comprehensive, universal health care system. The Canadian health care system is one of the few things that unite Canadians and something of which they are justly proud. However, reform is, and should be proceeding in order to deliver services where most needed, while keeping costs within a reasonable budget.

As reform has proceeded, physicians have often been cast into the problem category. This reflects the reality that each billing physician generates large costs to the health care system, not simply from the personal medical earnings, but more importantly because of the increased utilisation of health care resources. Consequently, reform has brought about an analysis of physician resources as they presently exist and numerous studies of future needs. There has not been consensus on the issues related to physician resources, but it is clear that the success of health care reform will depend a great deal on the success of appropriate physician resource planning.

Provincial governments in Canada have tabled the need for physician-resource planning for two reasons. First, to make health care services equally accessible to Canadians, within reason, by distributing physicians geographically and by discipline throughout the country with the rationale being that proximity to a physician will facilitate the appropriate entry of patients into the health care system. For the most part, all parties, i.e. physicians, government, and the general population, have accepted this broad principle, albeit to varying degrees. Secondly, and usually less clearly stated as a purpose, physician-resource planning, if it includes a reduction in physician numbers, will be used as a tool to reduce health care spending.

For purposes of this paper, I will focus on the role of the universities, i.e. medical schools in Canada, in making physician-resource planning rational and more likely to succeed. Firstly, I will outline the perspective that each of the parties interested in the issue has brought to the issue.

Physicians

As a group, physicians in Canada have viewed the planning of their numbers and distribution as a threat to their professional freedom. Although cognisant of the need for accessibility and financial constraints, they have been reluctant, even hostile parties in the process.

Government

As noted, provincial governments in Canada have as stated objectives for physician-resource planning, the issues of accessibility and cost containment. They have led the process, seemingly unilaterally at times, with varying success. It is clearly the intent of all the provincial governments to proceed with their local and potentially national plans.

In Quebec, the government has delegated responsibility to the regional health boards. The regional boards representing remote regions have an agenda with respect to physician resources which is different from the boards representing urban centres with teaching institutions.

The taxpayer

As the owners of the Canadian health care system, the taxpayer is demanding full access to health care without cost increases. As such, their wishes are generally consistent with those of the government.

The universities – faculties of medicine

To date, most faculties of medicine have viewed physician-resource planning as a potential threat to their academic freedom, a principle that remains fundamental to the university. The universities have as their responsibility, the teaching of future physicians and the purpose of new knowledge, both of which require precious time and money. In so far as physician planning has so far meant a reduction in the number of medical students and residents, which in turn represents a reduction in base budget and training programmes respectively, it cannot be surprising that such planning is seen as threatening to the medical schools. The consequent resistance to participation on the part of the universities and the lack of trust of the health care planners (government) in the universities (citing conflict of interest), has made a government/medical school partnership at best, an uneasy one and at worst, a non-existent one. Finally in this regard, the continued commitment of the universities to research and other scholarly activities, and the necessary human resources required to maintain this activity, can appear at least superficially, to be incompatible with the objective of physician resource planning.

Academic health centres or teaching hospitals

These institutions are, on the one hand, extensions of the medical schools, and on the other, they are providers of primary, secondary, and tertiary care – with the latter being almost exclusively in these centres in Canada. They also maintain a crucial role in the success of research programmes both within the hospitals themselves and through affiliated research institutes. With respect to physician-resource planning, therefore, these institutions complement the objective of the medical school, but will usually emphasise the service requirements more.

Physician associations

The physicians, both within and outside of medical schools, are represented by different bodies in each province which negotiate with government regarding their economic interests. More recently, in some provinces, such negotiations have included measures that will impact on physician distribution. The universities have not always felt well-represented by these various negotiating bodies which have served to isolate further the universities from physician-resource planning in some provinces. In Quebec, there are three such federations representing the GPs, the specialists, and the residents.

With this background, one can appreciate that bringing these different parties together is difficult and success in physician resource planning could easily be elusive. This paper will look at Quebec's history of physician resource planning, known as Effectifs Médicaux, over the past decade. It will illustrate its successes and failures and the changing role of the various stakeholders. In particular, the evolving role of the universities in the planning process will be traced.

Case study: the Quebec experience

Quebec is Canada's largest province geographically and the second-largest by population. It owes a huge debt which is growing. Quebec must address the issues of both accessibility and cost containment in the health care sector. Figures 1 and 2 highlight the problems with respect to physician distribution. In short, the specialists are centred in the large cities which are also home to the faculties of medicine. Certainly, this reflects concentration of advanced technologies in these areas which is, in large part, decided by government. However, there remain legitimate specialist shortages in some areas.

Conversely, in the areas of specialist concentration, there is a relative shortage of general practitioners, although some rural areas of the province are also short of general practitioners. There was consensus that, at least in part, this maldistribution needed to be resolved by moving specialists into the under-served areas. It was also anticipated that the numbers of specialists required in each discipline was not being met by the existing training programmes in the 1970s and 1980s. The following policies were therefore implemented over the past two decades.

To achieve an appropriate number (1:500 population) and type of physician

The number of medical students allowed each year is the subject of a government *décret*, and the number has been decreasing since 1981 with the total being about 15 per cent. The government *décret*, which designates to the universities the number of residency positions, started to include increasing restrictions as to how many positions could be filled in each of the various specialties. This was designed to try to match future needs and existing shortfalls within certain specialties. The movement of residents from outside Quebec for specialty training was restricted in numbers and these residents were asked to sign an agreement never to practice in Quebec.

Since 1993, medical students have been limited in their ability to receive 'J1' visas to train in the United States. This in theory, removes the option of students doing specialty training outside of the *décret* which is designed to respond to all of our physician-resource needs. To maintain further the closed box concept, i.e. those who train in Quebec can and will practice in Quebec within the terms of Quebec

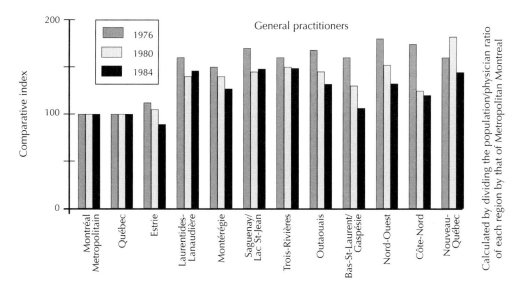

Figure 1 Comparison between the population/physician ratios for GPs of the various health planning regions and that of Metropolitain Montreal in 1976, 1980, and 1984

Source: Corporation professionnelle des médecins du Québec. Les effectifs médicaux du Québec. Montréal, 1986 (tableau 36)

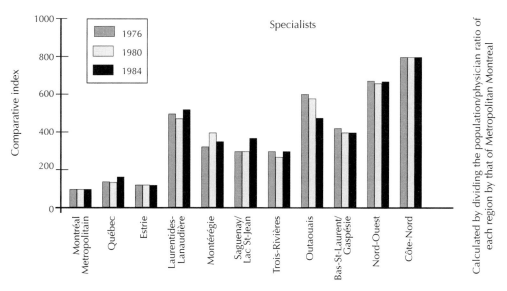

Figure 2 Comparison between the population/physician ratios for specialists of the various health planning regions and that of Metropolitain Montreal in 1976, 1980, and 1984

Source: Corporation professionnelle des médecins du Québec. Les effectifs médicaux du Québec. Montréal, 1986 (tableau 36)

planning (reflected by the *décret*), the origin of medical students in Quebec is also the subject of a *décret*. It defines not only the total number of students to be accepted by each university, but also from where they can come, i.e. Quebec, visa students, or other Canadians. Those from outside the province sign an agreement not to practice in Quebec. The number of non-Quebec Canadians allowed annually has decreased and most recently, in response to other provincial requests, Canadians outside of Quebec will not be accepted after September 1995. This position may soon be modified.

To achieve a better geographic distribution of physicians

Student bursaries were offered starting in 1975 in return for service in a distant area for three years. Differential fees were negotiated by the Federation of Specialists and the Federation of Omni-practitioners in the mid 1980s. This involved designating areas as under-served, neutral, and over-served by physicians. The MD fees applied in these areas were 120 per cent, 100 per cent, and 70 per cent respectively for the first three years that a specialist practised, and 115 per cent, 100 per cent, and 70 per cent for GPs. The physicians generally accepted the 'carrot' aspect of the agreement, but not the 'stick' aspect. The universities were able to negotiate an exemption for their recruits, allowing them to bill 100 per cent for anybody being recruited at the level of an assistant professor.

Active recruiting programmes were implemented by remote regions which included not only the financial incentives cited above, but also instalment grants, promises for continuing medical education, active community support, and assurances for appropriate back-up systems. A number of residency posts were put aside exclusively for contract positions, i.e. residency positions were granted contingent on a resident agreeing to practise in an under-serviced area for a minimum of three years.

By law, each of the nine regional boards was requested to develop a plan for *Effectifs Médicaux* in three-year cycles beginning in 1987. These plans are an assessment of need for physician services. As such, they should define the need both by geographic distribution and by the type of service. It is worth noting the methodology applied to make such an assessment of need. First, the billings (fee for service) for each specialty, including general practice, were tracked, totalled and averaged. This was used to calculate the number of full-time equivalents (FTE) in the specialty. The calculated number of FTEs was then increased by 10 per cent to recognise teaching, research, and administrative activities and this became the required number of specialists for the specialty. Each region and each institution was then assessed for the number of FTEs practising. The origin of patients utilising the services was also tracked through Medicare billings, thus providing for an assessment of how many services were consumed outside of the consumers' (i.e. patients') region.

This allowed for an assessment of the mismatch of need versus availability in each region. The *Effectifs Médicaux* plans were then designed to address and correct such mismatches. Future predictions of utilisation were corrected for anticipated demographic changes. As an example, this analysis has resulted in a plan for the island of Montreal for 1993–6 which calls for 97 more general practitioners and 44 fewer specialists, including a reduction of 13 psychiatrists. Not surprisingly, such a methodology with all of its inherent flaws, has to some extent distracted from the overall objectives of physician resource planning.

The *Table de Concertation* (round table) on medical manpower was created in 1986. It included all the different stakeholders including the Ministry, the regional boards, the federations, and the faculties of medicine. The *Table de Concertation* struggled in its first few years of existence with the participants disagreeing on which problems were to be dealt with, disagreeing on data sets, and disagreeing on solutions to mutually agreed upon problems. In 1991, the medical schools in Quebec proposed to the Ministry of Health and Social Services that they should collaborate in the planning of physician resources. They offered to do so by altering residency programmes to include community-based training, by offering the teaching hospitals as service back-up for the peripheral regions, and by offering appropriate continuing medical education for physicians in the outlying regions. This move on the part of the universities has facilitated the work of the *Table de Concertation* and more recently participants have reached agreement on solutions to some of the problems.

Clearly, from the above description of steps taken, the Ministry of Health in Quebec has been intent on making changes occur to effect changes in physician numbers (through medical student and residency numbers), in the type of specialists (through residency training programme restriction), and in physician distribution (through financial incentives and *Effectifs Médicaux*). It has done so by variably involving the universities, the federations (MDs' union), and the government bodies themselves (the regional boards) in the negotiations. But what has been the success of such plans? In part, one cannot answer the question as it is impossible to know what the distribution of physicians would be in the absence of such measures. To be sure, fewer MDs are graduating, which will mean fewer practising physicians and therefore presumably less cost to the health care system.

It is apparent that in Quebec the success in managing specialty physician-resource issues only started to take hold in 1987 and became substantial after 1990. The decade preceding 1987 introduced a decreased student enrolment and a number of measures negotiated with the Federations, but these were inadequate measures to meet the objectives. What then changed in 1987 which has allowed success?

I would argue that it has been the active participation of the universities through the Deans of Medicine and their associates, that has allowed true reform in physician-resource planning to proceed. On reflection, this should not be surprising since the medical schools are the source of all physician resources. The medical schools, through their curriculum and role models, introduce to the students their career options. For the residency programmes they provide the tools and experience for future practice. And through the medical schools' leadership role, they offer the linkage for all physicians to continuing medical education and to changing technologies and back-up for patients across the entire province. There is an interdependence between all physicians, the medical schools, and government health plans. This must be recognised and taken advantage of in order for successful reform to continue. The recognition of this interdependence in Quebec, with the formation of the *Table de Concertation* and regional board subcommittees on *Effectifs Médicaux* at which university leadership is evident, has allowed physician resource planning to proceed and, at the same time, has allowed the objectives of both the health care planners and the universities to be maintained.

Risks remain for the university in this process of physician resource planning. Uncertainty remains as to the impact of *Effectifs Médicaux* on the medical schools and teaching hospitals mission with respect to teaching and research. Shrinking numbers of students and residents and the restrictions on recruitment for attending staff are all potentially serious threats. The outcome may take years to assess but if the effect is to limit academic activity seriously, this will have been a high price to pay. The price will not simply be to the universities themselves, but to the health of our citizens at large. The government needs to acknowledge that the pursuit of new knowledge in the universities is a legitimate objective that complements the health care system. Equally, the universities must acknowledge the legitimate need for redistribution of medical services through appropriate planning of MD resources. The obvious interdependence of the two parties in this process has started to be accepted in Quebec and has allowed new and more effective means of managing the issue.

In conclusion, evolving health care reform depends in part on the successful management of physician resources. There are a variety of stakeholders in the issue, including the government, the taxpayer, the physicians and their unions, the universities and the teaching hospitals. All claim legitimate ownership of the issue, but a successful outcome will depend largely on active participation and consensus between the universities (medical schools) and the government health care planners. Quebec's experience over 15 years in implementing policies aimed at altering physician numbers, type, and distribution highlights the need for this coalition. Real success was achieved only when the universities became serious partners in the issue, rather than peripheral to it as has often been the case previously.

Health sector reform in South Africa
and the development of a district health system

&- *Tim Wilson* -&

⟶ Editor's comment

Perhaps the country which is undergoing the greatest change is South Africa, where the end of apartheid also means enormous change in health care delivery. Wilson outlines the background of South Africa as well as the political changes of the entire system. Health care is only one aspect of a difficult and slowly changing situation.

Although South Africa is a middle-income country which spends an average of US $210 per capita per annum on health care, disparities are great. Many of these disparities are reflected in economic and racial divisions, despite recent changes from the apartheid system.

Wilson describes the process of health care reform to the apartheid system officially beginning with the ANC's conference on health policy in 1991. By 1993, the focus was on 'inter-sectoral collaboration' and included groups focusing on health care reform. After consultations, conferences and drafts, the Reconstruction and Development Programme (RDP) emerged. This general plan of change is currently being implemented.

Wilson describes the evolution of a district-based health care system, applying it to local government, primary care services, the private/public mix. Specific problems encountered include fragmentation of service delivery between local organisations, and differences between the new and the old systems. Although the new policies may be emerging as dominant, many implementers are of the old system. These 'old officials' are also receiving higher salaries than those of smaller authorities. This variation in salary is manifested in terms of quality of service available, becomes a constant source of friction, and hinders the integration of service delivery.

Some suggestions have been: to regionalise the district services to metropolitan councils and rural councils; to delegate them to 20 health districts within each province; or to establish district Health Authorities.

cont.

cont.

Wilson calls on the prospect of emphasising local governance as opposed to local government. While he celebrates the new structures introduced to improve child health care among others, Wilson suggests that there is a lack of attention being paid to individual facilities. Changes, therefore, are not occurring everywhere: poor local conditions, low staff-morale and ability, and lack of additional resources, mean that the positive changes are not being felt everywhere at the ground level.

Despite these disparities – the extreme differences of culture, value and vision – there remains a shared agenda. Diverse groups recognise and seem to appreciate their differences, but are still prepared to work on these very issues in health care.

Background

South Africa, with a population of nearly 40 million people, is a middle-income country that spends 8.5 per cent of its GDP on health care. Three years ago it was already spending an average of about US $210 (R740) per capita per annum on health care. These averages of income and of health care expenditure, however, disguise enormous disparities and inequities within the society. The existence of a government of National Unity, the remarkably peaceful transfer of political power and the strong spirit of reconciliation must not be confused with progress towards equity. They certainly assist the process, but by themselves they do nothing to make health care more accessible to the majority of South Africans.

The problems are made more difficult by the fact that the wealth of the country was squandered in the last years of apartheid. Between 1989 and 1994, the outgoing government borrowed heavily and made almost no effort to contain its rising recurrent expenditure. In only five years, repayments on debt, expressed as a percentage of total government expenditure, jumped from less than 10 per cent to more than 25 per cent. This severely restricts the new government's ability to restructure the budget.

Statistical information on the whole country is generally of poor quality, especially for the rural areas and the former 'homelands'. Unemployment is estimated to be above 50 per cent, under-employment is very common and there is no social security net. Nearly 60 per cent of the total population have incomes below US $86 (R301) per month, but the proportion who live below the Minimum Living Level ranges from 2 per cent for whites to 65 per cent for the residents of the former TBVC homelands.

Although nearly half (47 per cent) of the population live in the rural areas, only a tiny fraction of them are still subsistence farmers. The vast majority of the people in the rural areas are totally dependent on the urban economy for survival. The main resources in the rural areas are the people, the money spent by migrant workers and other relatives, and the meagre old-age pensions. It has been estimated that, on average, about 12 people depend on one old-age pension.

The disparities between the rich and the poor are clearly reflected in levels of health expenditure and in the indicators of health status and determinants.

Health expenditure in the private sector is around US $750 per capita per annum (p.c.p.a.) for the 17 per cent of the population covered by medical schemes (private medical insurance). In the public sector, however, it is about US $150 p.c.p.a. in the Western Cape Province and only about US $50 p.c.p.a. in the Northern Transvaal Province. Even within these new provinces, levels of expenditure vary greatly, and for some communities the real level of expenditure is probably close to US $5 or US $10 per capita per annum. In both public and private sectors the bulk of the money is spent on curative care, with 81 per cent of the health budget going to hospitals.

Considering the relatively high GDP and high average expenditure on health care, South Africa does spectacularly badly on most health indices and still has 12 million people, 30 per cent of the population, who do not have access to clean drinking water. Infant mortality rates (IMRs) and other indices vary enormously between communities. The average for the country is 49 per 1000 live births but for white people it is around 12 per 1000, while for black people it varies from around 35 in major urban areas to more than 100 per 1000 in some rural areas. The average maternal mortality rate per 100,000 live births is eight for white people compared with an estimated 58 for Africans. The rate will be much higher for Africans in rural areas. Although no cases of polio have been reported since 1989 and immunisation rates in most communities are around 70 per cent, tuberculosis has remained a major killer even before the advent of the HIV epidemic, and AIDS is going to create huge social problems.

The inefficiency of South Africa's health care system is shown in the Table 1, comparing South Africa with five other middle-income countries. This, and most of the other information on expenditure, is taken from the recent Health Expenditure Review published by the Health Systems Trust and the World Bank.

Both the public and the private health care systems are extremely fragmented. This has resulted in a great deal of duplication, huge gaps, and enormous wastage, and has contributed to the current crises in both sectors.

In the public sector, fragmentation has been taken to incredible lengths. There were 14 independent 'national' departments of health. In 'white' South Africa, four of these 'national' departments provided some services, while four provincial health departments ran the public hospital services. In addition, there were more than 800

Table 1 Comparison of South Africa with other middle-income countries

Health spending (percentage of GPD)	Infant mortality (per 1,000)	Incidence of TB (per 100,000)	Life expectancy (years)
South Africa **8.5**	Malaysia 15		Chile 72
Hungary 6.0	Hungary 16	Hungary 38	Malaysia 71
Chile 4.7	Chile 17	Venezuela 44	Hungary 70
Venezuela 3.6	Venezuela 34	Chile 67	Venezuela 70
Botswana 3.3	Botswana 36	Malaysia 67	Botswana 68
Malaysia 3.0	**South Africa** **49**	**South Africa** **250**	**South Africa** **63**

local authorities, half of which had health departments that ran preventive and promotive services and had 15 different salary scales; but there were also large areas of the country that did not fall under any local authority. Another problem is that over the past ten years the previous government made almost no investment in infrastructure. Many of the hospitals and clinics that were in good condition ten years ago, have been handed over to the new government in a shocking state of disrepair. Finally, there was a blind faith in the dogma that 'private is efficient and privatisation is the answer', and 'Limited Private Practice' was introduced in the medical schools.

The crisis in the private health care sector is rather different from that in the public sector, but is even more serious. Here the problem is rather one of uncontrolled, third-party fees for a service system that is collapsing. Greed, over-capitalisation, fear of falling incomes and lack of any coherent national policy has led to gross over-prescribing and over-servicing, particularly with expensive investigations such as MRI scans. The rate of inflation in the costs of private health care in recent years has been 27 per cent, two to three times the general rate of inflation in the country. In ten years medical aid contributions increased from 7.1 per cent of salaries to 15.2 per cent of salaries. Medical schemes were faced with rising costs and falling membership as young people found medical insurance unaffordable. This was compounded by rising unemployment which also decreased membership.

Several schemes went bankrupt and many patients and doctors found that members had reached the limit of their cover. In 1993, shortly before it lost power, the previous government responded by amending the relevant Act to allow individual risk rating. But while this may bring short-term relief to the young, it does nothing to addresses the underlying problems and at the same time starts to erode the whole concept of risk sharing. There is a real danger that the whole medical insurance industry could collapse.

Political advances in the past five years

Over the past five years, the people of South Africa have made tremendous advances in their long struggle for justice. The struggle against apartheid was often seen, particularly from outside, as a struggle against racial discrimination. It was that of course, but it was also much more. The struggle was, and is, for justice, for equity and for a decent quality of life for all. It is also a struggle for democratic participation in all forms of governance from national parliament to local clinic and school committees.

South Africans used to refer to 'the system'. 'The system has arrested and tortured so and so.' 'The system is busy privatising.' 'The system has introduced a new health act.' This was accurate. Apartheid was a whole system, a whole culture, a whole way of doing things. Everything about health care in South Africa was contaminated by 'the system'.

The authoritarian nature of the health services, the discrimination against women, the huge gap between the salaries and conditions of service of professional staff and those of support staff, the centralised decision-making, the under-funding of services for the poor and the over-provision of services for the rich, the gross disparities in services between urban and rural areas, and many other problems that the new government now faces, were all part of the system that was known as apartheid. There are two reasons for emphasising this. Firstly, to make it clear that the struggle against apartheid began long before the National Party came to power in 1948, and it did not end when everybody voted on 27 April 1994. This date was a milestone and a very important milestone, but it is only one milestone on a very long road. There are other milestones further back along the road, some good ones and some bad ones, and there will be other milestones on the road ahead. The struggle continues.

The second reason for emphasising the comprehensive nature of the apartheid system is to make it clear why the vast majority of South Africans are determined to push ahead with a total transformation of all aspects of our society. Health-sector reform is only one part of a much bigger picture of social transformation.

Many of the problems listed above also occur of course in other countries. But in South Africa, because they were so intimately associated with the old system, there is the opportunity now to throw them out along with the philosophy and practice of apartheid. Three of the questions that have to be answered are:

- Strategically, which are the best issues to tackle first?
- How long will the window of opportunity remain open?
- How quickly can we change without causing the whole system to collapse?

The process has been likened to the need to replace all the rotten bottom planking of the ship, while keeping it sailing through rough seas, and trying not to get your feet too wet.

Creating and managing the environment for change

Building consensus before the election

Apart from the general political atmosphere which favours transformation, there have been nearly ten years of work to build consensus on what sorts of change are needed in the health sector. Long before the unbanning of the ANC in 1990, as the pressures for change mounted in all sectors, people in the broad democratic movement were recalling the findings of the Gluckman Commission of the 1940s and were promoting ideas and developing services that could serve as models for components of a more efficient, effective, and equitable national health system based on the primary health care approach. Their efforts were then caught up and carried forward by the massive movement that accompanied the unbanning of the African National Congress (ANC) and other organisations.

The first ANC National Health Policy Conference was held in January 1991 and several ANC regions presented papers advocating a national health system. This was followed by the production of a draft policy paper that was widely distributed and was discussed at the ANC National Conference in July 1991. Discussion continued in 14 regional conferences, comments came in, a new draft was produced, discussed in detail at the ANC Policy Conference of 1992, and was amended and adopted by 3,000 delegates as the health section of the ANC Policy Guidelines. These were published and widely distributed throughout South Africa in the booklet *Ready to Govern*. Discussion with people outside the ANC began with the distribution of *Ready to Govern* and led to informed and useful debate.

The process of putting flesh on the bones of the guidelines then began in earnest early in 1993. A series of workshops were organised by the ANC Health Department. These involved representatives of all 14 regions of the organisation but also drew in representatives of other organisations in the broad democratic movement such as trade unions, civic organisations, NGOs, and research institutions. The first workshops identified 11 priority areas for policy development, each region worked on some or all of these areas, national task groups were formed and several national workshops were held on each policy area.

At the same time this was all going on, senior members of the ANC Health Department were meeting with a wide range of people from other departments in the ANC: from the pharmaceutical industry, the medical aid schemes, professional associations, the medical schools, the Medical Research Council, and from the government Department of Health. The principles laid down in *Ready to Govern* were explained and debated, and some of the ideas emerging in the policy working groups were discussed. Each discussion and debate influenced the next one and the whole process helped to build a large measure of consensus.

In the second half of 1993, work began on developing ideas across all sectors on a proposed plan for reconstruction and development. This again involved a number of people from the ANC Health Department, several of whom were actively involved in the process of health policy development. The emphasis here was on intersectoral collaboration and the process was driven jointly by the ANC, by the Congress of South African Trade Unions (COSATU), and by the South African Communist party (SACP). What emerged, after six drafts, wide consultation, a national Conference on Reconstruction and Strategy, and much public and private comment, was the Reconstruction and Development Programme (RDP). This was published early in 1994, before the election, and was subsequently endorsed and adopted by all parties in the government of National Unity. The health section of the RDP clearly reflects the principles outlined in *Ready to Govern* and the ideas in the second draft of the National Health Plan.

At the same time as the RDP was being developed, the process continued of co-ordinating, consolidating and refining the national health policy. By the end of October 1993, there were ten policy documents that were debated at a national workshop, and a group was elected to turn them into one plan. The first draft plan was circulated within the broad democratic movement and discussed at yet another workshop in December 1993. The second draft was produced in January 1994 and was released widely for comment by all interested parties. There was a massive response and written comments came in from a very wide range of role players. One of the most striking features of these responses was the broad acceptance of the principles of the plan, and the constructive comments made by almost all respondents on ways to improve the plan.

The final result of all these comments was the third draft which was formally endorsed by the ANC and was published in May 1994 as *A National Health Plan for South Africa*. There were obviously many people who disagreed with some of the details, but a remarkable degree of consensus had been built-up and most people in the health sector accepted the plan as the best way forward. Within a year, 10,000 copies had been distributed and a reprint had been ordered.

Managing change since the election

One of the important implications of the present South African 'revolution' is that the whole society is 'unstable' in the sense that everybody expects change. People are much more prepared to accept major changes now that they are likely to accept in five years' time. There is a momentum for change which presents a tremendous opportunity for people in every sector, including health, to perform radical surgery on the system where it is needed. In this context of social transformation, the challenge in the health sector is how to ensure that we move beyond mild reform and grasp the opportunity to transform the health sector also.

We are fortunate that within the governments of National Unity at national and provincial levels, the portfolios for health have all been given to members of the ANC. This makes co-ordination easier but it also perhaps indicates an acceptance by other parties of the ANC's vision for health and health care. The Minister and her provincial counterparts share a common vision of fighting for equity and for one unified health system that:

- is based on districts and a primary health care (PHC) approach;
- draws in the local authorities, the NGOs and the private sector;
- is organised at central, provincial, and district levels;
- makes an integrated package of essential PHC services available to the entire population.

They have begun the process of consolidating the old national, homeland and provincial health departments into a single system, of redistributing the budget in a more equitable way, and of drastically changing health care priorities so that integrated primary health care, with its community orientation and its attention to priority health problems, becomes the order of the day. A number of committees have been established to look at important areas of policy, and a major national investigation and debate has been started on the question of health care financing and the possibility of a National Health Insurance system.

The first steps taken were to redefine the functions of the provincial and national health departments, to create new post structures that reflect these functions, and to advertise all the management level posts. This has been a massive task with about 300 of the most senior management posts in the health sector being advertised. Many of these posts are now being filled with people who have a new vision of health care and are committed to the primary health care approach. Most candidates were scheduled to take up their posts by May or June 1995.

This is all good, but there is also a cost. During the process of restructuring it has been very difficult to improve the running of the provincial and national health departments. All existing staff in these departments have found the process very unsettling, and it has been difficult to know who should make what decisions. Many of the new managers lack management experience, and one of their greatest challenges will be to motivate existing staff to build effective teams.

Building the district health system

Local government

At the district level, the position is even more complicated. The interim constitution created nine new provinces with clear boundaries and elected legislatures, but it did not create any districts. It did create local government, but is ambiguous about its powers. The main parties to the negotiations that led to the democratic national and provincial elections agreed that there should be elected local government in all parts of the country, but they could not agree on how it should function, or even how it should be elected, and so they left several difficult questions aside.

Under the old regime, the 800 local authorities, mainly in 'white' South Africa and all employing their own officials, had very little credibility with the majority of the population. They were responsible for, and administered, many aspects of the apartheid system, and they often did so harshly. Large parts of the homelands and 'white' farming areas had no local authorities: the farmers ruled on their farms; and most homelands had a system of chiefs. These chiefs were all appointed by the previous governments and they drew salaries like civil servants. Although some were traditional leaders and highly respected by many people, many others were not. The chiefs wielded considerable administrative and judicial power in their locality, many of them resisting handing over these powers to elected local government.

In the run-up to the first democratic elections for local government, scheduled for 1 November 1995, the demarcation boards in each province were busy drawing boundaries. The main concerns of senior politicians charged with getting local government established were firstly persuading the majority of the population that it is worth registering to vote in local government elections at all, and, secondly, persuading the chiefs to allow free and fair registration and voting in their areas. Arguments about the best form of governance for district health services were not their prime concern. The electoral boundaries suggested by the demarcation boards would bring black and white together, but they usually fail to link the urban areas with their surrounding peri-urban and rural areas, and therefore they are mostly not suitable as the boundaries of health districts.

About 500 local government areas are being suggested. The urban areas are quite well resourced and will take over the infrastructure of the old white local authorities, including all their staff. Most of the rural areas, by contrast, have little or no administrative infrastructure.

There is a danger that while urban areas continue to build on their infrastructure and benefit their local residents, people living outside the town boundary will continue to receive poor services because of a lack of local infrastructure. Linking rural services with those in the town where the rural people shop and bank and do their business, would create much greater equity.

Primary health care services

The homeland governments ran reasonably comprehensive services but in the rest of the country most primary health care (PHC) services were, and still are, fragmented, with the old local authorities providing preventive services, the provinces providing curative services and the national departments overlapping here and there. It is quite common for the staff of two or three different authorities to work in adjacent buildings, or even in different parts of the same building, and to run completely separate services. Up to five different Health Authorities may run a variety of PHC services in the same town.

There is political commitment and pressure to devolve as much power as possible to local government. At the same time, there is a real fear in the health sector that this will perpetuate old inequities in service delivery, with urban areas having reasonable resources and rural areas getting very little. There is also concern that the attitudes of most officials have changed very little so far and that it will be extremely difficult in the short-term to replace more than a handful of them. The vast majority of those who come into contact with the health care system do so at the district level, and there is concern that they will see very little change if all the old officials remain in place.

At the heart of the problem are the differences in salaries and conditions of service among the old local authorities, and between them and the provincial governments. Senior staff in the large local authority health departments earn much higher salaries than their counterparts in the smaller local authorities or than equivalent staff in the provincial health departments. Terms and conditions of service also vary enormously. These differences are a constant source of friction. They are also a major source of inequity because the larger (urban and metropolitan) local authorities pay better salaries than the smaller ones, and so can attract more qualified staff. Several attempts have been made in the past to get staff employed by different authorities in the same or adjacent buildings to work together, but each time the experiment has failed to get off the ground because of the differences in salaries and conditions of service.

The ultimate objective of the government is for integrated PHC service to be controlled and managed at local level. All nine provincial health departments have started a process of district development. This has included establishing, in each province, at least five or six district facilitation committees that have embarked on ambitious programmes of meetings with local communities and other stakeholders. The process has gone well in most provinces and there is considerable local support for district development.

One suggestion is for district level health services to be put in the hands of metropolitan councils and rural district councils. Each of these will co-ordinate the work of a number of local authorities; they will cover large areas of the country and they will contain, on average, about one million people. Problems with this option include getting services stuck with a body that is still very distant from people in communities but will have a vested interest in not devolving services any further, and potentially continuing disparities in salaries and conditions of service.

Another suggestion is for all district level services to be retained for the time being at provincial level, to divide each province into about 20 functional health districts, each with a population of about 200,000 people, and to develop clear programmes of delegation, capacity building, and local governance at district level. Bringing all staff on to the provincial establishments would be one of the fastest and cheapest ways of moving to a uniform set of salary scales. The problems with this option are opposition from some very vocal existing local authority officials and, more seriously, a concern that this represents centralisation which will never be reversed.

A third suggestion is for the creation of 'District Health Authorities' (DHAs) that are distinct from the provincial and local governments. A DHA could cover the area of two or three or even more local governments, elected representatives from the constituent local governments could sit on it, and it could employ all district level staff in its area. The first problem with this option is that it will take time, and legislation, to create these DHAs and to establish an administrative infrastructure. The second problem is that these DHAs could easily start to function as independent parastatals and this could give rise to new forms of fragmentation.

Local governance

The key to solving the problem of who controls the district may lie in promoting local governance rather than local government.

The first step is to delegate authority and responsibility for budgets, and for day-to-day running of services, to local managers. At the same time, boards and committees can be constituted to advise these managers on local policy and on budget priorities. Ideally, each facility within a district will have its own board, consisting of local residents. As the relationship develops, these boards or committees can become statutory bodies. They can then assume responsibility for approving budgets and for determining local policy, within national and provincial frameworks.

If the District Health Authority (DHA) option is pursued, all local government structures in the district will be represented on the DHA. It then becomes less important who actually employs the staff who work under the DHA.

Public–private mix

A suggestion has been made that District Health Authorities should be able to fund both public and private providers of primary health care services, and thereby draw private providers more closely into the district system. Private providers could be 'accredited' if they fulfilled certain criteria such as providing a comprehensive range of services and functioning as a team. Accredited providers would be paid a capitation fee by the DHA and would have access to essential drugs at state tender prices.

Other doctors would work full-time or on a sessional basis in public clinics and health centres, as at present. In some small towns where it is not possible to recruit a doctor to work in the public sector, nurses in the health centre could refer individual patients to a private doctor for specific treatment if necessary.

Private providers could still operate independently, funded by the medical insurance industry or by cash payments, but there would be a strong incentive to form group practices and join the public system.

The system suggested can be represented schematically as shown in Figure 1.

Other actions and problems

At the service level, gross discrimination has been reduced, access has been improved by making care available free of charge to children under six years of age and to pregnant women, a feeding scheme has been introduced for five million children in primary schools in impoverished areas, and a clinic upgrading and building programme has been started. But with so much attention being given to new structures, there has been very little time for improving matters within individual facilities. So far, the new government has failed to improve conditions or to provide additional resources for, or to build capacity of, staff at local or district level.

There is widespread realisation that there is a serious lack of the skills required to reach the objective of full local management and to deal with the organisational changes, the integration and devolution of services, and the greater emphasis on increased efficiency and equity. Some progress is being made in this area with a number of courses being developed which are of direct relevance to health managers, and most provincial health departments have begun to establish their own human resource planning and development sections, but much greater co-ordination at the national level is required.

One of the biggest problems is that although referral systems exist, there is no uniform or universal referral system in support of primary health care. Where such systems do function, they are often inefficient and costly. Some provinces have started to plan the development and implementation of a proper referral system at primary, secondary, and tertiary levels. Other provinces are developing plans to improve the efficient use of existing transport and to explore the use of alternative transport systems.

Finally, a number of changes are essential at district level to improve staff morale and effectiveness. These include the recruitment of staff, improved conditions of service, incentives to work in rural areas, orientation of new staff to community services and comprehensive health care, and in-service education. Perhaps most important of all is developing a common vision and welding all staff into a single and enthusiastic team.

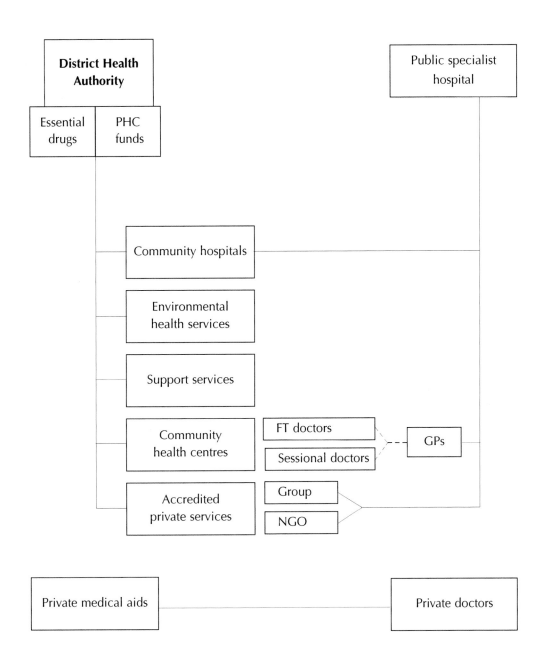

Figure 1 District Health Authority funding of providers

Conclusion and issues for debate

South Africa has started on the right road but still has a very long way to go to build a district health system that reaches all the people of the country.

If, as seems likely, the District Health Authority option is pursued, the major issue will be how much autonomy should the DHA have, and how soon. In the long run, will competition between different DHAs promote efficiency or fragmentation, or both? Could they go the route of becoming one or more parastatal organisations, or must they stay within the public service?

The advice of people who have faced these issues before, and who are committed to equity, will be much appreciated by South Africans as they move towards making decisions that may affect several future generations. As it was expressed in the election slogan: *Now is the time.*

Not-for-profit providers and network development

❧ Frederick D Alley ☙

➤ Editor's comment

Fred Alley's paper recognises the problems with managed care and suggests that a network of providers might be able to come together to resolve some of them. What he proposes is not restructuring, but new ways of working that take into account the varying interests and perspectives of different providers. The disadvantage of such networks is clear: they are more difficult to 'manage' than a single organisation with established values and control mechanisms. But we have learned that getting rid of the boundaries between organisations does not assure unity of value or perspective. Indeed ignoring the differences in 'unified' organisations is a major source of 'unmanageability' in health care. Whoever said it was going to be easy?

Alley enters into the debate about managed health care. What are the ramifications of privately funded health care systems? Will the public good be served? Will those who already can't afford health care be pushed away even further? Fred Alley proposes provider-initiated networks as a solution. Here the purpose is not the restructuring of a system but the development of collaborative relationships between providers. Alley's model is defined through a series of analyses determining the needs of the community as seen by the providers and the physicians, who come together in an affiliation and identify programmes which will result in an integrated delivery network.

Alley explains that Physician–Hospital Organisations (PHOs) allow for the discussion of critical issues among key players within the health care sector. After each region has established its own PHO, these affiliates can be brought together to create a Super-PHO which 'represents the ultimate marketing tool for an integrated delivery system'.

The actual form of the network may vary. For example, these could be medical centre networks incorporating both hospitals and academic centres or not-for-profit affiliations such as HealthFirst, a managed health care body which provides a 'mechanism for each (member) hospital to assume full risk in the managed care market'. In this example, the

cont.

> *cont.*
>
> network provides the marketing and other services, while the hospitals provide service delivery.
>
> The opportunities grow once these networks are in place. Large-scale projects can be undertaken which may not have been possible by single members. There are further economies of scale: more programmes can be made available and better performance can be recognised. Such networks also allow for mid-size providers to be involved in an integrated delivery system.

Overview

As President and Chief Executive Officer of a 653-bed, voluntary, teaching hospital located in a medically under-served community in New York City, the diminishing prospects of broad-based reform of the American health care system have reminded me of *Alice's Adventures in Wonderland*. You may remember, as Alice came upon the Cheshire Cat, she asked his advice on which path she should take. 'That depends,' he answered, 'on where it is you want to get to.' Alice didn't care where she went and the cat replied that in that case it didn't matter which path she took. 'But,' said Alice, 'I want to get somewhere.' 'Well, then,' was the cat's advice, 'sure to do that if you only walk long enough.'

Fortunately, those of us in the health care industry, unlike Alice, have the benefits of our shared experience and some degree of foresight to help us determine the direction in which to go. As in the rest of the United States, hospitals in New York City face increased pressure to provide a higher quality product for a lower price and to a larger patient population. For hospitals that serve the wealthy and middle-class, and hospitals that serve the poor, these pressures are forcing a re-examination of the structure and underlying principals of health care delivery. Hospitals across New York City are forming new kinds of relationship and alliance in response to the new challenges. These new relationships are transforming New York's health care delivery system and increasingly affecting the flow and distribution of patients across health care institutions, even in the absence of reform.

The legacy of *non*-reform in the United States

Real reform has yet to come to fruition in the United States. Increases in health care spending continue to outpace growth in the GDP and pressure is mounting to reduce spending even in the absence of legislated reform. This creates both opportunities and challenges for health care institutions. Without uniform or nationalised health care policies, each market or locality is free to develop that system which best serves the needs of both patients and providers.[1] However, localities must do so without the administrative and financial support that a national system and uniform policies would provide. While some localities may be able to predict the needs of their patients accurately and are well-prepared to balance these needs with the needs of physicians and health care institutions, others may not have sufficient resources to do so.

In the United States, and in New York State in particular, the absence of nationalised or uniform legislation has made it possible for innovative providers to pursue new and diverse visions of integrated delivery systems. The experience of providers in New York State sets the stage for a discussion of what may be most appropriately titled 'After Non-Reform, What?'. In New York State, at least, the answer has been for providers to pursue the creation of integrated networks and systems that meet the demands of the market-place (cost containment, quality, and continuum of care) while enabling many institutions to continue to fulfil the obligations of their voluntary mission to provide care to all who require it, regardless of ability to pay.

So, after *non*-reform, what? The answer lies in creating an entirely new system of health care delivery and economic modelling that meets the demands of the new market-place and functions in the interest of the public good.

In the United States, market forces have begun to replicate many of the intentions of national health reform without the bureaucracy, and, unfortunately without the fiscal and administrative support of the national policies in place in other countries. At the same time, few states and localities have developed the regulatory checks and balances that can shape system development while protecting both providers and patients. Many states and localities have reduced health care spending drastically without regard to the needs of the not-for-profit health care sector. Many voluntary and not-for-profit providers in the United States thus are experiencing economic free-fall with pressure to reduce costs radically and shift existing economic resources away from hospital-based acute care. While these pressures intensified as the debate over health care reform grew louder in 1993 and 1994, they have not abated despite the failure to implement viable reform.

In New York State, economic pressure on voluntary and not-for-profit providers is exacerbated by a for-profit insurance industry, health-maintenance organisations (HMOs) in particular, who demand deeply discounted rates and remove capital from the system. For example, prior to the introduction of for-profit Medicaid managed care corporations, the Medicaid reimbursement structure included payments to providers for capital expenses and on-going financing of the public good through charity care and medical education. Rather than keeping this capital in the system by decoupling capital reimbursement from capitation rates, the reimbursement structure has remained virtually unchanged. For-profit entities by their very nature cannot put the public good first. Yet these 'public good' payments are now channelled to the managed care corporations and HMOs and are no longer available to the actual providers of care.

Based on the experience of The Brooklyn Hospital Center and other urban teaching hospitals, I believe that regardless of the future of national health care reform, provider-initiated networks must come to dominate the health care market-place in New York State and represent a viable alternative to the for-profit dominated systems present elsewhere in the United States.

The 1990s thus represent a transitional period of opportunity between New York State's current health care system and one that is network oriented. Many components of the transition are already in place: regional purchasing alliances and coalitions, multi-provider networks, integrated physician/hospital partnerships, shared-risk contracting, and capitated insurance products. Models for a number of these alternatives are already in operation elsewhere in the United States.

This paradigmatic shift is driven not only externally, by market forces and health care reform at the state and local level, but also internally by the strategic actions of innovative providers and payors who are forming integrated networks that can deliver a continuum of care and manage financial risk. This internal movement stems in part from mounting demand by private and public purchasers for more cost-effective and accountable health care services. From my experience with integrated networks and from discussions I have had with other health care executives, all evidence suggests that the integration of financing and care delivery with the alignment of economic incentives offers the most sound approach to achieving clinical efficiencies and improving clinical outcomes, establishing administrative economies, and creating effective managed care contracting even as we provide demonstrable community benefit.

This paper will begin with an overview of the market-place and various alternative network configurations, and then detail three of these configurations as they relate to The Brooklyn Hospital Center's experience. The paper concludes with a model for provider-initiated networks based on the experience of The Brooklyn Hospital Center.

Health care market-place

The health care market-place in New York State has been highly regulated and one in which health care institutions have, by design, had small or negative operating margins and little access to new sources of capital. At the same time there has been an incredible downward pressure on health care spending and an increased focus on managed care as a solution to spiralling health care costs. But how is the environment in New York State different from the environment elsewhere in the United States or in other English-speaking countries where governments have not abdicated their responsibility in setting national health care policy?

As an example, in both California and Minneapolis, Minnesota, health care institutions enjoyed considerable operating margins and access to capital before capitated systems were introduced. For-profit health care providers and aggressive insurance companies were both present in the market. The for-profit sector capitalised on changes in the market-place and established strong footholds in the market. Systems and network development were driven by insurers and the for-profit provider industry. After decades of changes, California and Minneapolis now have high rates of managed care penetration and low-cost systems. But these systems are dominated by the for-profit sector. Institutions with missions to provide care to the under-served have been forced in many instances to compromise these missions in order to continue to operate. Improved public health has become a means to an end of cost control, rather than an end in and of itself.

The unique environment in New York State, however, has not allowed such a shift. For-profit hospitals and health care institutions are not yet permitted to enter the New York market.[2] Although state and local spending cuts will reduce reimbursement, public and not-for-profit providers none the less have a tremendous market opportunity to redesign the system and take full advantage of the reimbursement structure to keep operating surpluses and capital pass-throughs within the system. Public and not-for-profit providers can then use this capital to reinvest in the community and implement measures to further improve community health.

The tightly regulated nature of New York's health care system and the absence of investor-owned or other for-profit providers, however, provides few opportunities for infusing new capital into the system. The operating margins in New Jersey, Florida and Texas are from 5 per cent to 9 per cent.[3] New York's providers must seize available opportunities quickly and efficiently to streamline operations, improve their own operating margins, and consolidate and align economic incentives across networked institutions. Only then can they make significant improvements in public health and continue to be viable institutions in light of reduced reimbursement opportunities. As New York moves into an increasingly capitated environment, providers have a unique opportunity to develop provider-sponsored integrated delivery networks and systems that enable them to take full financial risk, effectively keep all excess revenues within the system and available for reinvestment, and thereby measurably improve community health status.

Network responses to the shifting market-place

Based on the experience of The Brooklyn Hospital Center and other hospitals in the United States, a continuum of network development has been outlined (*Figure 1*).

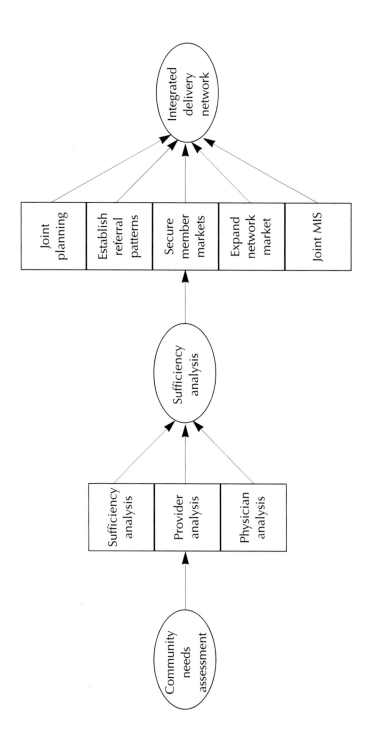

Figure 1   Provider-initiated networks

Although New York embraced managed care in 1986, fast-paced growth in managed care activity has only occurred in the last two to three years in response to cost-containment initiatives. In the three years since the introduction of Medicaid managed care programmes, enrolment has grown to more than 20 per cent of all Medicaid recipients.[4] Medicaid and commercial managed-care entities are being created by both for-profit insurance companies and not-for-profit alliances of health care institutions.[5]

Traditional HMOs also have gained a foothold in New York since their introduction in 1986. Indeed, just last year the number of New Yorkers enrolled in HMOs surpassed the 25 per cent mark of all those with health insurance.[6] An enrolment level of 25 per cent is considered a benchmark for HMO activity because at this rate nearly all consumers in a system know at least one person who is enrolled in an HMO and the presence of HMOs in the system is accepted by most consumers.

The advent of Medicaid managed care and the introduction of HMOs have radically altered the landscape for New York's health care institutions. Hospitals with more than a century of comfortable, though modest, operating results find themselves competing for market share for the first time in their history. Smaller and younger hospitals are being courted actively by larger, academic medical centres who offer everything from faculty appointments for physicians, to capital infusions, to group purchasing discounts, to free advertising. Most hospitals, free-standing clinics, medical schools, and even small groups of physicians, are scrambling to ally and enlist partners in 'networks'[7] of all sizes and configurations.

The array of provider-initiated networks in New York State demonstrates what providers are capable of achieving if they act quickly and decisively as soon as their market-place begins to change to favour networks. In California and Minneapolis, providers did not move quickly enough and these markets are now dominated by insurers and for-profit entities.

Network development

In this paper, I will examine horizontal networks in which two or more hospitals are involved. Loosely defined, horizontal networks comprise those networks in which services may be duplicated between participants in order to cover a wider patient-base. Horizontal networks enable network members to secure their existing markets while increasing the market share of the network as a whole.

In addition to horizontal networks, a number of vertical configurations have also arisen in the United States. In vertical networks, participating institutions divide responsibility for services, with little or no duplication between institutions, to create a continuum of care. Examples of the components of vertically integrated networks include: affiliations with community, neighbourhood or satellite primary care health centres; hospital-based out-patient clinics; affiliation with private practices; provision of secondary and tertiary hospital care; home care; and affiliation with one or more long-term care facilities. In New York State, vertically integrated networks are already appearing and will begin to proliferate within the next five years.

In 1994 and 1995, participation in various network configurations was surveyed by the Greater New York Hospital Association (GNYHA).[8] The survey covered 56 member hospitals and the results highlight some interesting trends. Eight-two per cent (46 hospitals) report participation in at least one network or system. Of these, nearly a third participate in two or more networks.

In a 1992 survey of hospital CEOs across the United States by *Hospitals* magazine, 72 per cent said that their hospital is either collaborating with or planning to share services with another hospital.[9] This proportion holds true for urban, suburban and rural areas alike. For example, 80 per cent of CEOs of Virginia hospitals report some participation in network systems.[10] The Brooklyn Hospital Center has had experience with a variety of network configurations that demonstrate the requirements for success.

Affiliation and integration of large acute care institutions

In 1994, The Brooklyn Hospital Center entered into a clinical and academic affiliation with New York University School of Medicine and Medical Center (NYU). With the assistance of the consulting firm of Ernst and Young, the Hospital and NYU examined the possibility of joint support systems that would secure each institution's existing market share, establish a wider composite market share for the system, and provide some degree of administrative cost savings. Several other hospitals in the New York City metropolitan area (also affiliates of NYU) were also asked to participate: Lenox Hill Hospital, Orthopaedic Institute, and Beekman Downtown Hospital.

The first step in formulating a network was to begin joint planning efforts to examine three key areas: clinical relationships and referral patterns; joint development of community-based primary care networks to secure each institution's existing market and to expand the system's combined market; and exploration of joint services to try to achieve administrative savings through combined Management and Information Systems (MIS), billing and purchasing.[11]

An essential step in the integration of these affiliated hospitals is creating a physician-management structure that is satisfactory to the physician groups and that is organised in a fashion that permits smooth contract negotiation and implementation.

The benefits of integrated systems for hospitals and physicians include:

Hospitals	*Physicians*
◆ Bolstering market share and creation of a vehicle for growth	◆ Maintainance of market share and growth in managed care
◆ Effective competition with other systems for capitated contracts	◆ Provision of access to capitated contract/avoidance of lock-out
◆ Tightening of utilisation to improve risk pools	◆ Reduced risk
◆ Market leverage *vis-à-vis* payor community	◆ Provision of access to hospital capital/management expertise
◆ Attraction of primary care providers to market	◆ Reduced administrative burdens

As the New York City metropolitan area market becomes increasingly focused on capitated models, a shift from an in-patient/fee-for-service focus to one that is out-patient-focused and primary-care-driven is occurring. Integrated systems in this market must, therefore, redesign current configurations of physician contracting and practice patterns. The NYU affiliates currently are examining the mechanisms available to redesign their physician base and make physicians an essential part of the management structure of the system. Ideally this redesign will begin as Physician–Hospital Organisations (PHOs) at each affiliated hospital and progress to a Management Services Organisation (MSO) for the entire integrated system.[12]

At The Brooklyn Hospital Center, the PHO takes the form of a 'Managed Care Board' with representatives from Hospital Center administration, each clinical department, and the major physician group practices. The Board is chaired by the Vice President for Managed Care, a physician who also serves on the Hospital Center's senior administrative body. The existence of this PHO has enabled the Hospital Center to move swiftly into the managed care market-place and secure contracts with numerous payors and, at the same time, begin the development of its own managed care product. The existence of a PHO provides a forum for physician/hospital discussion of critical issues related to the managed care environment while encouraging the alignment of economic and administrative incentives between physicians and the hospital. At the same time, working with the PHO has enabled the Hospital Center to build mutual trust and positive working relationships with the physician leadership.

As other hospitals in the NYU affiliation begin to explore establishing PHOs, several factors must be addressed to ensure success. Final authority for signing managed care contracts must rest with one person. There must be a balanced role among various physicians and physician leadership groups, emphasising primary care. PHOs should carefully consider restrictions on physician membership and contracting options outside the PHO. Finally, effective management of data is critical to any system planning to enter a capitated environment.

Once each affiliate has developed a PHO that is suitable for the needs of their communities and physician base, the affiliates' PHOs can be brought together to form a 'Super-PHO' with authority to act on behalf of the entire system. This Super-PHO may take a variety of forms, from simply a conglomeration of affiliate PHOs, to an independent HMO, to a multi-level managed care corporation. Whatever the structure, a Super-PHO represents the ultimate marketing tool for an integrated delivery system, enabling affiliates to increase significantly their ability to enter into managed care contracts while at the same time consolidating administrative costs and responsibility associated with physician and managed care consulting.

Members of the NYU affiliation group are now looking beyond PHOs to a real integrated delivery network encompassing a wide geographic area and member institutions with vastly different patient bases and physician specialties. The development of this network has been an evolutionary process. The affiliation partners are now exploring the creation of a management corporation that will facilitate real network development. We don't yet know what form this arrangement would take. It could be a corporation that manages all network activities. It could be a corporation that owns all the member institutions. In the next year we will examine the benefits and limitations of many such arrangements.

Of course, there are some legal restrictions on relationships of this nature. In the United States, anti-trust concerns can interfere with integrated network development. Integrated delivery networks must therefore involve significant sharing of risk between hospitals, and PHOs must operate with at least 20 per cent withholds or capitation. Physicians must have some right to opt out or, as an alternative, the network may be set up in such a way that a third corporation is created to make decisions for hospital and physician interests. Finally, board representation or voting systems must ensure that physicians do not have inappropriate control of decision-making.

Medicaid Managed Care networks

In response to the Medicaid Managed Care directive in New York State and the rise of other managed care programmes, the most common network arrangement reported in the GNYHA survey is that in which participants share ownership or equity interest in a managed care organization. In the United States, networks of this type are expected to increase in response to the growing number of state-wide Medicaid managed care programmes. Twenty-six states already require Medicaid enrolees to participate in managed care programmes and another ten offer voluntary programmes. At least 12 additional states are planning Medicaid managed care programmes.[13] In New York State, what was implemented by a democratic administration with an eight-year phase-in to 100 per cent Medicaid managed care enrolment has been transformed by a new Republican Governor to require nearly 100 per cent enrolment almost immediately.

The Brooklyn Hospital Center has responded to the introduction of Medicaid managed care by forming, with other voluntary providers, and alliance to facilitate provider-sponsored entrance into capitated systems. HealthFirst was originally conceived as a joint venture of 11 hospitals to create a Pre-paid Health Services Plan (PHSP) that would give participating hospitals the ability to take full risk in a capitated system. Each institution contributed to the capitalisation of the company and to designing a plan that would serve each institution's patient base. While each institution assumed full financial risk for enrolees, there was no shared risk between institutions. New York State, however, intervened on the grounds that the arrangement was too loose and required there to be more risk-sharing across participants.

HealthFirst thus became a closed network where all business and referrals took place within the network and participants were not permitted to contract for services outside of HealthFirst. HealthFirst is now a hospital-owned and controlled managed care network of 17 hospitals, each with equity interest in the managed care corporation/PHSP.

Basically, HealthFirst is a not-for-profit managed care entity that operates as an HMO for the benefit of its 17 member hospitals. Member hospitals own the corporation and have equal votes in the Board of Directors. Decisions are made by majority vote, or, in the case of bylaw modification, by super majority. HealthFirst performs all of the functions of a traditional HMO, under the direction of the Board of Directors, utilising various corporate and licensing arrangements. Through HealthFirst, member hospitals accept full capitation in a PHSP subsidiary for the purposes of Medicaid, and eventually will be able to participate in a HealthFirst HMO subsidiary for Medicare and commercial insurance. Member hospitals are required to provide a capitalisation of $400,000 to HealthFirst, and, are obligated to provide an additional $200,000 if necessary, with the approval of a two-thirds majority of the Board. This level of participation will allow HealthFirst to break even.

HealthFirst anticipates having enrolled a total of 323,000 participants with revenues of $895 million by 1998. Participation is expected to consist of: 183,000 Medicaid enrolees, 67,000 Medicare enrolees, and 67,000 commercially-insured enrolees. Self-funded commercial enrolees would be in addition to this total. In 1998, the average member hospital will receive through HealthFirst (excluding self-funded lines of business) 19,000 members.

The advantages to participation in this type of network are evident. HealthFirst provides a mechanism for each hospital to assume full risk in the managed care market. HealthFirst performs common marketing, member services, utilisation review, claims processing, and MIS, while participating hospitals provide service delivery. Finally, HealthFirst offers a co-ordinated response to dealing with the requirements of both Medicaid managed care and a traditional commercial HMO market. Network members participate in a not-for-profit holding company which operates as a PHSP subsidiary for Medicaid and will operate as an HMO subsidiary for Medicare and commercial insurance contract.

Regional networks

The Brooklyn Hospital Center's participation in the Voluntary Hospitals of America Metro New York (VHA) network is a regional extension of the Hospital Center's arrangement with NYU. VHA is a regional integrated delivery network that consists of three hospital clusters, each with a major academic institution at its centre.

The function of VHA is to enhance the ability of member hospitals to carry out their respective missions as independent, high-quality, free-standing, not-for-profit institutions. Initially, joint purchasing was a primary force and function behind VHA, but the network has since expanded to a network of independent yet linked providers with the capability of offering or arranging for a full range of services throughout the New York metropolitan area. Thus, individual VHA hospitals are strengthened in their local markets, and the network as a whole can better meet the needs of purchasers throughout the region in a cost-effective manner.

But VHA does not exist solely for the benefit of member hospitals. Voluntary hospitals can and should have an important role in improving overall community health and acting to promote the interest of the communities we serve. Since VHA is a strong, commercially-viable network of voluntary rather than for-profit, proprietary hospitals, we have the option, and indeed the obligation, of reinvesting in the communities we serve. Many examples of such reinvestment exist across the network: for example, community-based training and scholarship programmes and community outreach and education programmes. This reinvestment is due, in part, to revenues in excess of expenditures arising from reduced costs for goods and services obtained through the network.

There are 12 institutions currently networked via VHA. They vary from a small community hospital in rural, wealthy Southampton Long Island, to academic research centres such as New York University Medical and Columbia-Presbyterian Medical to large urban teaching hospitals such as The Brooklyn Hospital Center.

In our experience with VHA, perhaps the most important factor in successful network development has been in-depth market research and planning. As hospitals across the United States face tighter operating budgets due to local, state and federal reductions in reimbursement, such market planning will become even more essential to successful network integration.

For example, VHA undertook a network sufficiency analysis in 1993. This sufficiency analysis was premised on the assumption that a network needed a minimum of 25 per cent of all discharges within a market to be a 'market force'. VHA tried to identify, by market segment, which other hospitals VHA needed to add to its network to achieve this minimum 25 per cent market share. VHA then sought out new potential network members with the following selection criteria in mind:

- the fewest number of hospitals to achieve the 25 per cent minimum of discharges within the market segments;
- the fewest number of hospitals to achieve a minimum of 25 per cent for each of the major payor classes (Medicare, Medicaid, commercial) when matched with the discharges of network hospitals in the market segments;
- the fewest numbers of hospitals to achieve a minimum of 25 per cent of discharges and the lowest possible cost per case.

Once we identified potential network affiliates, we then compared network sufficiency with and without these potential affiliates and then compared both of these scenarios with the network sufficiency of other networks in the New York City region.

Although this sufficiency study provided significant insight into potential network affiliates, we realised that such an analysis was incomplete. In the new managed care environment, our market share study, which was based on in-patient discharges, failed to consider other factors which affect network sufficiency. For The Brooklyn Hospital Center, this meant examining physician network capability in addition to provider network and distribution capability.

Some of the questions to be considered in an analysis of physician networks are:

- Can 'surplus' physicians in one region be used to cover need in an adjacent area?
- Can physicians be taken from other hospitals, and, if so, at what levels?
- What areas can be reasonably targeted without adding hospitals?
- What resources are available for physician recruitment and salaries?

Of course, any study of a network's physician capability must account for physicians who practise both primary and specialty care and for physicians with multiple hospital affiliations. Thus far, based on its network sufficiency study and on our physician network capability study, VHA has developed a Primary Care Provider (PCP) coverage strategy for Manhattan and Queens which identifies areas that are under the 25 per cent target and begins to address possible methods for bringing these areas up to 25 per cent through marketing efforts, physician relocations, second offices, and outreach to physicians already on staff at member hospitals.

Once these issues have been addressed and a viable network is in place, the benefits for participating institutions are many. Through co-operation and joint planning the opportunity exists for the development of large-scale programmes that could not readily be accomplished by individual members. At the same time, most member hospitals experience an enhanced patient market share due to the broad regional and specialty coverage available through the network. This type of network also offers specific benefits for the institution looking to maintain autonomy while improving quality of care and market performance. These benefits include: cost reduction through shared resources, integrated programmes and a group purchasing plan as well as improved academic programmes and diversity of exposure for medical students and residents. Additionally, since member hospitals are not being asked to surrender fiscal or administrative autonomy, and, indeed, are encouraged to develop new specialty programmes as part of the affiliation, we have been more successful in recruiting high-quality affiliates.

VHA Metro New York has had some specific successes as a result of network affiliation which have brought many benefits to the member hospitals. A cluster of member hospitals located in Westchester County have organised into a sub-network of VHA called the Westchester Health Services Network for the purpose of contracting with self-insured employers in the distinctly defined market-place of Westchester County, New York.[14] Although seeking out self-insured clients in Westchester did not make sense for the network as a whole, this sub-network was able to use the resources and experience of VHA in establishing contacts with employers there. The Westchester Health Services Network's first client has been the Westchester Schools Cooperative Health Program. Four VHA member hospitals are involved, with more than 1,000 participating physicians and providers.

VHA also has enabled member hospitals to advance in the managed care market. In 1994, Chubb Life, a private, institutional insurance provider, decided to co-ordinate with a Health Maintenance Organisation (HMO) to create a new managed care product for the New York market called Chubb Health. Chubb struck an exclusive deal with VHA to use VHA hospitals in exchange for negotiated rates. Although the member hospitals are autonomous in delivery of services, the fact that this deal was able to be negotiated by the VHA network presented an opportunity that no member hospital would have had on its own. The benefits to Chubb are indisputable in the tremendous geographic coverage provided by an extensive network such as VHA.

Finally, VHA is seeking ways to enter the managed care market-place directly. The TriState Health Network represents the transformation of VHA from a joint purchasing group into a managed care delivery system. It is through this network that VHA will pursue obtaining an HMO licence in the future.

But what have been the disadvantages to network arrangements such as VHA Metro New York? There is the absence of uniform control. However, as long as basic standards are agreed upon as part of the network agreement, network configurations allow individual hospitals to respond to the particular needs and talents of their medical staff in terms of compensation, recruitment, and performance review. Also, The Brooklyn Hospital Centre has found that there can be a difficulty in allaying medical staff fear of take-over as a result of network participation. However, because the relationship is a network rather than a merger, participating hospitals can more openly represent the interests of their own medical staffs. Negotiations with medical staff should also take into consideration the importance of Physician–Hospital Organisations (PHOs) in making decisions regarding the inclusion and exclusion of physicians. Physicians at each member hospital are required to have a physician-governing body that allows VHA to negotiate on behalf of physicians and hospitals as a single unit. This is one way to involve physicians in decision-making. Finally, patient commerce issues can be a problem, for example the loss of non-specialty patients to a more conveniently located network partner. But, for VHA the key to avoiding each of these disadvantages has been a well-developed network agreement.

Conclusion

The experience of The Brooklyn Hospital Center demonstrates that with careful planning and a thorough investigation of the local market, even mid-size providers can take advantage of the opportunities presented by integrated delivery systems. As national health care systems in other English-speaking countries undergo reform and restructuring, providers who have pursued network and system approaches aggressively will be most able to absorb the impacts of these changes and continue to operate in the best interest of the communities they serve. Although administrative and reimbursement structures vary widely from country to country, the underlying principles of network development can be applied to almost any environment.

This paper provides a basic overview of what's out there in terms of network affiliations, and the benefits and pitfalls of these arrangements. However, as someone who has been on the front line, negotiating these agreements, trying to sell them to our medical staff and working out the logistical headaches created by integration, I can tell you that although I truly believe that these arrangements are the way of the future in health care in the United States, successfully implementing any new system can be incredibly difficult in ways that are hard to predict.

Notes

1. The terms 'health care institution' and 'provider' will be used interchangeably throughout this paper to refer to hospitals, medical centres, and clinics.
2. Prior to 1986, Health Maintenance Organizations, a key feature of the California and Minneapolis systems, were essentially prohibited from the New York market since the regulatory system did not allow for discounted reimbursement. In New York State, all commercial rates are related to Medicaid reimbursement and the absence of share-holder ownership of hospitals is still prohibited.
3. American Hospital Association.
4. Commercial managed care products have experienced similar rapid growth.
5. In New York State, insurers have entered the Medicaid managed care market with fully-capitated plans modelled on traditional HMO arrangements. Prepaid Health Services Plans (PHSPs) were created to enable health care institutions to also participate in Medicaid managed care at full risk. For the most part, groups of hospitals with common interests, such as the hospital of the New York City Health and Hospitals Corporation or the hospitals in the Catholic Medical Center system have allied themselves to provide Medicaid managed care services through such PHSPs.
6. *New York Times*, 25 March 1995, pA1.
7. For the purposes of this paper, the terms 'network' and 'system' will be used interchangeably to describe a wide variety of inter-institutional arrangements.
8. Greater New York Hospital Association survey of member hospitals, April 1994 and March 1995.
9. *Hospitals*, 20 April 1992, p60.
10. *ibid.*
11. The experience of other institutions attempting to reduce administrative costs through network affiliation has indicated that savings of only 4–6 per cent are possible.
12. A 'Physician–Hospital Organisation' (PHO) is an equal partnership between a provider or system and its physicians to build trust, secure joint managed care contracts, and operate effectively in a managed care environment. The presence of a PHO greatly enhances the ability of providers to negotiate contracts quickly and efficiently with payors. A 'Managed Services Organisation' (MSO) is an organisation that provides practice management and comprehensive physician services to physicians affiliated with the integrated delivery system.
13. *Medicaid: States Turn to Managed Care to Improve Access and Control Costs.* Washington, DC: United States General Accounting Office, 1993.
14. Westchester County is one of the wealthiest counties in the United States. A significant percentage of professionals who work in New York City reside in Westchester County. At the same time, Westchester County is home to several large Fortune 500 corporations such as IBM.

Conclusions

This book began by looking at hospitals in 1935, 1955 and 1985, and at the many changes around health care systems and organisations: changes both in organisations themselves and in the participants who play the various roles in health care. All these changes made reform more urgent. They also affected our views of the environment and organisations.

The 1935 organisation occurred in an essentially understandable world, one in which we could tame nature by coming to understand its physical laws. The well-functioning organisation was a smoothly running command-control Taylorian machine which could be understood and directed by one chief. An apple orchard could be planted on command.

In 1955, the world surrounding organisations was still thought to be essentially understandable but more complex: it required specialised expertise which would give us the answers. The division of intellectual labour would still produce a Utopian future based on the understanding of the laws of nature and we would gain ultimate control over it. Organisations now contained a number of specialist functional hierarchies to manage specific areas. The apple orchard was thriving with the expert help of an orchard keeper.

By 1985, organisations became less sure of their capacity to understand the world completely. Although in physics the essential uncertainty of our knowledge of the universe was widely recognised, this view had not yet had an impact on our understanding of organisations. Knowledge was becoming too fragmented. In health care, the systems were now hopelessly complex and apparently out of control. The medical superintendent's apple orchard was in deep trouble. The hope was now to re-integrate the organisations and systems in order to regain control. Reform of one kind or another became the answer, and not only in health care.

It was believed that the problems associated with health care organisations and systems were structural. And there were widely accepted procedures for planning and implementing the strategies to change them. Stakeholders had to be identified and consulted. Mission, vision, and values had to be declared, made uniform and corporately sanctioned. Appropriate changes could then be made to put the new structures in place. Once everyone was 'on board' it would no longer be necessary to struggle with differences in values and perspectives. Rigid professional and institutional boundaries would be reduced or eliminated. Rational evidence-based plans could be implemented.

Although often attempted, these methods seemed not to work. There were always stakeholders who were somehow excluded. There seemed to be no acceptable shared mission or vision, unless it was so watered-down as to be meaningless. There was rarely full agreement on evidence for decisions. Despite numerous major structural changes, the problems seemed to remain and become even more intractable.

The first series of papers in this book indicates also that there was no single direction of reform. In some countries the effort was to decentralise authority; in others to centralise it. In some it was to increase government regulation and funding; in others to decrease it. In some it was to create many more smaller institutions; in others to create fewer large ones. This scattered approach suggests that it might be necessary to go beyond the existing reforms and find new ways of thinking about the organisation of health care. The King's Fund International Seminar was an excellent vehicle for this kind of thinking.

We are beginning to think that the scientific views which accept instability as an essential ingredient of the universe have some application to organisations. It is not that things are out of control and we must institute measures to control them, rather we must recognise that they are not subject to the older notions of control and new ones must take their place. The book contains many of these new ideas.

Structural change is not enough. In this book we have tried to look at how reforms have affected health care systems and organisations. We have tried to think about the impact of the reforms and whether this can give us a better understanding of these organisations and systems. The book does not come to a resolution. Instead it draws several lessons.

Learn to work across boundaries

We now recognise a much greater interconnectedness of all parts of the physical world. Part of the difficulty comes from this. Increasingly our understanding brings us back to the many connections between health and health care and, as they say, 'everything else'. The boundaries between hospitals and the rest of health care are fuzzy and growing fuzzier. The tight external boundaries of the 1935 hospital are no longer tenable. And inside hospitals, the divisions between specialties are changing. Attempts to strengthen them are counter-productive. The distinctions between hospital and community, between health and social services are becoming harder and harder to identify. When they are marked out, it seems that regardless of how it is done, there are always some undesired consequences, usually to some vulnerable population or other.

We must accept this fuzziness as the context for our deliberations and ask ourselves how to accept the differences that occur across traditional boundaries. We must work across such boundaries rather than trying to redefine them.

Recognise and accept differences

If it is acknowledged that providers of health care have different training, expectations, values, and even language, then, in order to work across the boundaries of their many disciplines, they must learn to accept and respect these differences and a diversity of views. Solving problems can only occur in a context where these differences are better understood and respected. It may be possible to share an agenda rather than a vision or mission, as in the case of work with Aboriginal people. It may be necessary to hear the views and perspectives of far more groups because of the many connections that exist, rather than persuading or forcing everyone to adopt a single vision or set of values. It may be necessary to spend more time understanding and appreciating the different kinds of knowledge and evidence that are brought to bear on health care issues and debates. There is no doubt that all this seems more difficult than restructuring, but it does recognise that the problems result from real differences rather than inadequate structural designs.

Create collaborative networks

Health care systems and organisations are intimately linked with the other social structures and even beyond them. The first two lessons are steps on the way to building more lasting and productive relationships between individuals, professions and organisations. Changing and improving the relationships between these unique groups is not a structural issue. Indeed, forcing widely differing groups into the same structure does not help them work together. Collaboration between such a variety of perspectives is difficult. It must occur while respecting the differences and in most cases, the boundaries between them. The messiness, instability, and unpredictability of these relationships mirrors the rest of reality. But as in other areas, this instability does not obviate the possibility of high levels of organisation and effectiveness.